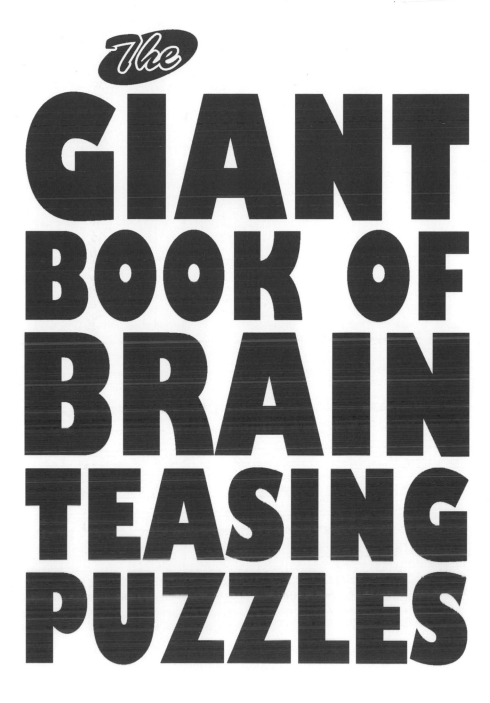

The GIANT BOOK OF BRAIN TEASING PUZZLES

EDWIN GODWIN

Capella

This edition published in 2007 by Arcturus Publishing Limited
26/27 Bickels Yard, 151–153 Bermondsey Street,
London SE1 3HA

Copyright © 2004, 2006 Arcturus Publishing Limited

ISBN-13: 978-1-8193-627-7

Cover design: Steve Flight

Printed in Malaysia

Contents

The Giant Book of Brainteasing Puzzles is packed full of math and word puzzles for children of all ages and abilities. Both sections have been divided into 5 levels or chapters: in the math section, 1 is the least difficult and 5 the most challenging, whilst in the word section there is a real mix and match with easy and not-so-easy puzzles side by side in each chapter.

In the math section the grids and shapes that make up the puzzles are the same in each level, although as you work your way through the book you will need to use different methods (i.e. addition, multiplication) to solve them.

We suggest you start both sections at level or chapter 1 and work your way through puzzle by puzzle. Take your time and don't worry if you can't do a puzzle at your first attempt—you can always come back to it later. You will see that some of the tougher questions have clues to help you and also that both sections have the answers at the back, although try not to look at them before you have finished unless you are really stuck!

Feel your confidence grow as you get the answers right and move onto the next level. Soon you will have reached the end and won't even have needed to look at the answers.

Finally, to help you on your way, here are some handy hints for the math section.

- Look for patterns in the numbers
- Prime Numbers are numbers that can only be divided by themselves or 1
- Square Numbers are numbers multiplied by themselves (2 x 2, 3 x 3, 4 x 4 etc.)
- Cube Numbers are numbers multiplied by themselves three times (2 x 2 x 2, 3 x 3 x 3, 4 x 4 x 4 etc.)

ODD ONE OUT

Which number is the odd one out in each oval?

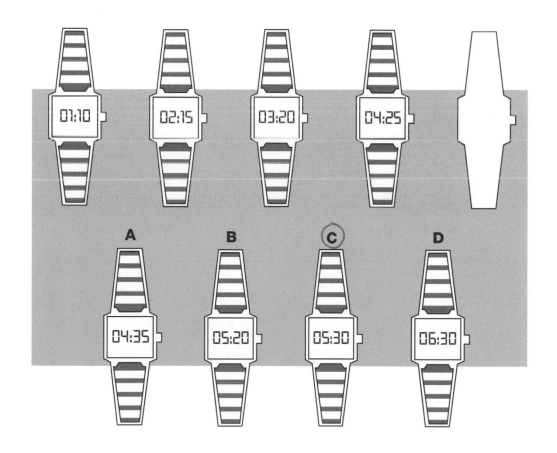

WATCH OUT

Look carefully at the sequence of watches and fill in the blank.

3

PYRAMID POSER

Work out what number goes at the top of the third pyramid.

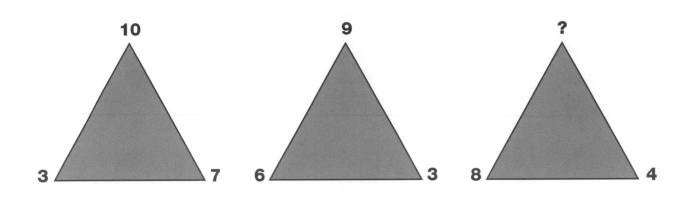

10
3   7

9
6   3

?
8   4

 4

ALL SQUARE

Here is a complete puzzle—work out why it contains these numbers.
(Clue: The center square holds the answer.)

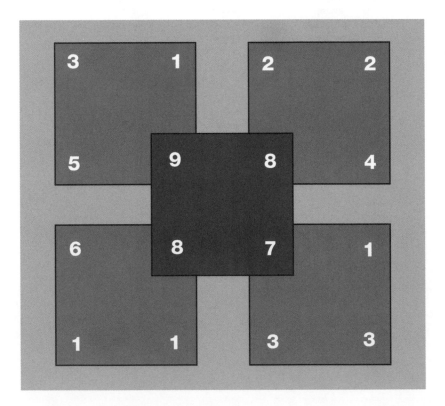

3   1
5   9   8   4
2   2

6   8   7   1
1   1   3   3

DOTTY DOMINOES

By counting the dots on these dominoes, can you work out
which of the six spare pieces completes the sequence?

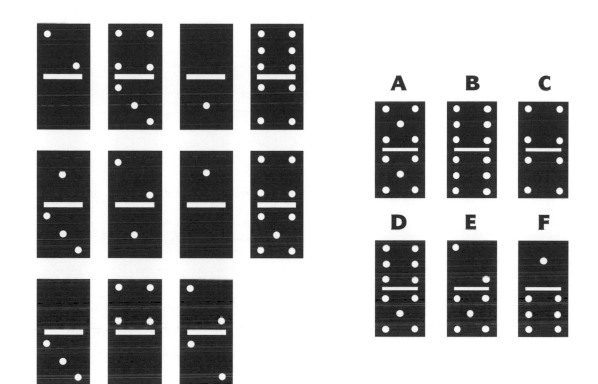

CROSS OVER

What number is missing from each puzzle?

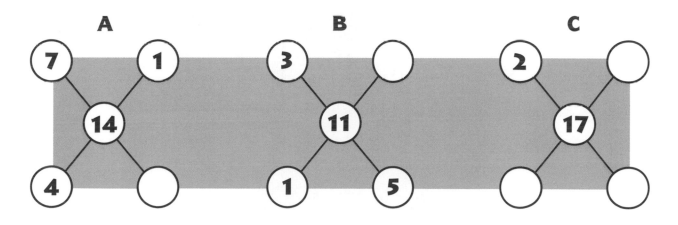

7 TRI—PIE

What number is missing from the empty segment?
(Clue: Look at the matching segments on each circle.)

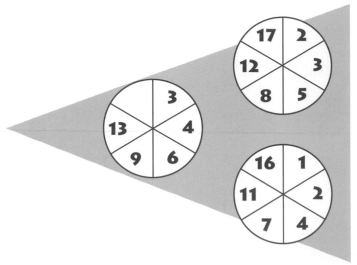

8 NUMBER BOX

Complete this number box by adding the correct number.
(Clue: The puzzle works up and down as well as side to side!)

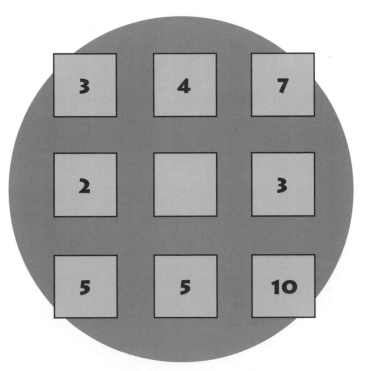

WEB WORLD

What number replaces the question mark and completes the web?
(Clue: Try rotating part of the web.)

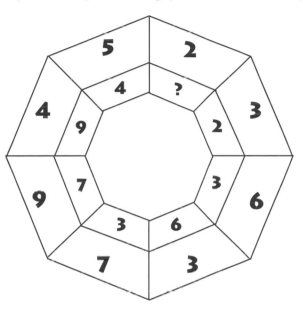

MAGIC SQUARE

Fill in the empty circle and complete the puzzle.
(Clue: Look carefully at the grid to find the pattern.)

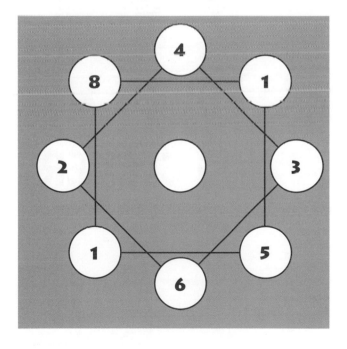

ALL STAR

By using the first two stars as a guide, can you complete this puzzle?

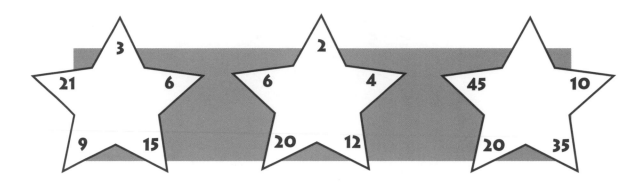

CIRCLES

What number is needed to finish the puzzle?

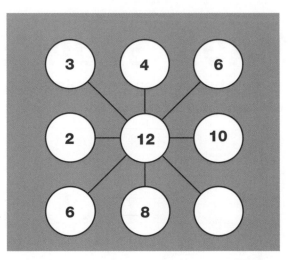

BOXING CLEVER

What number completes this sequence?

MISSING NUMBERS

What numbers are missing from the empty grid?
(Clue: Look at the matching segments—the middle circle is the link!)

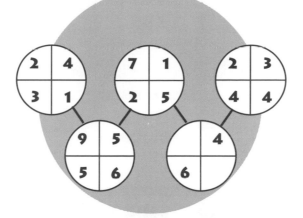

HONEYCOMB

Which number is the odd one out?

HOLE NUMBERS

Complete this puzzle by adding the correct number to the empty circle.
(Clue: Straight thinking will not help you with this one!)

FIGURE—IT—OUT

What three-figure answer is missing from the empty box?

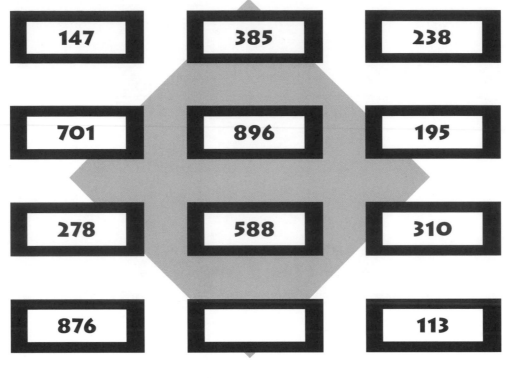

147	385	238
701	896	195
278	588	310
876		113

SHAPE UP

Find the missing number to complete the puzzle.

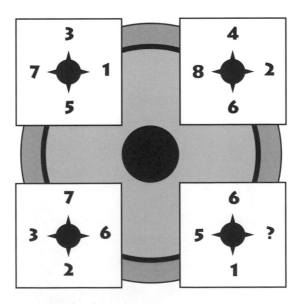

TAKE AWAY

What number goes in the middle oval?
(Clue: It has got nothing to do with sums!)

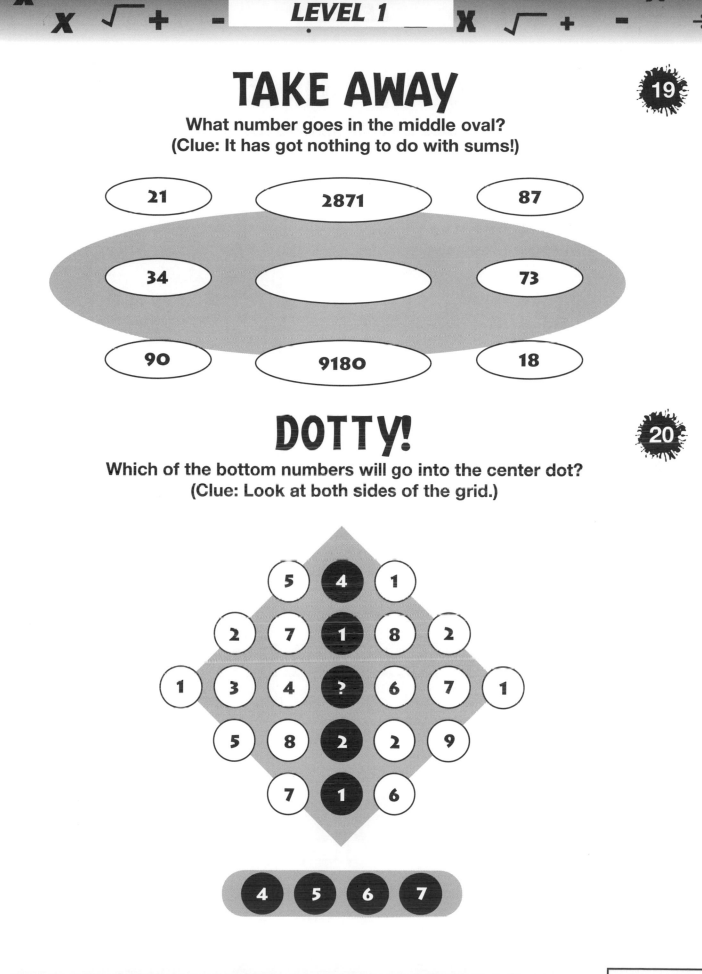

19

21   2871   87

34   73

90   9180   18

DOTTY!

20

Which of the bottom numbers will go into the center dot?
(Clue: Look at both sides of the grid.)

```
        5  4  1
      2  7  1  8  2
    1  3  4  ?  6  7  1
      5  8  2  2  9
        7  1  6

      4   5   6   7
```

ROGUE NUMBER

In each square we have added a rogue number.
Can you work out which one it is?

A

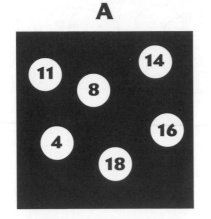

11 14 8 4 16 18

B

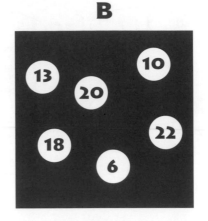

13 10 20 22 18 6

C

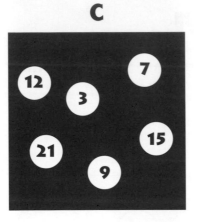

12 7 3 15 21 9

D

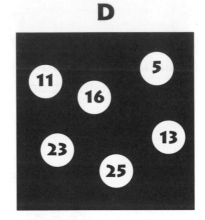

11 5 16 13 23 25

MISSING LINK

What number completes this chain?

3 5 8 12 17 23 30 ?

LINE UP

Using the same rule for every row, can you fill in the empty octagons.

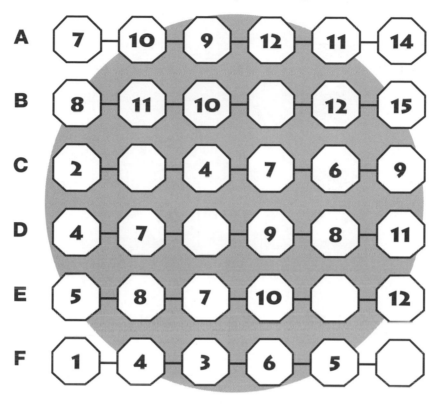

A 7 — 10 — 9 — 12 — 11 — 14

B 8 — 11 — 10 — ( ) — 12 — 15

C 2 — ( ) — 4 — 7 — 6 — 9

D 4 — 7 — ( ) — 9 — 8 — 11

E 5 — 8 — 7 — 10 — ( ) — 12

F 1 — 4 — 3 — 6 — 5 — ( )

CHANGE IT

Replace the question mark with the correct number.
(Clue: Look at the relationship between the numbers in each segment.)

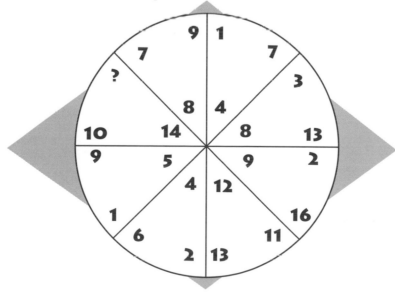

9 | 1
7   7
?   3
8 | 4
10   14   8   13
9   5   9   2
4 | 12
1   16
6   11
2 | 13

25

OPTIONS

Which of the three numbers at the bottom will complete this puzzle?
(Clue: Try looking up and down.)

3	18	21
6		24
9	12	27

11   15   21

 26

NUMBER SQUARE

By using every number between 2 and 10 can you complete this number square so that every line, up and down, left to right, and diagonal adds up to 18?

	10	
4		
		7

STAR STRUCK

Using the first two stars as an example, find the missing number.

TRIO

Using the first two circles as an example, fill in the empty segment.

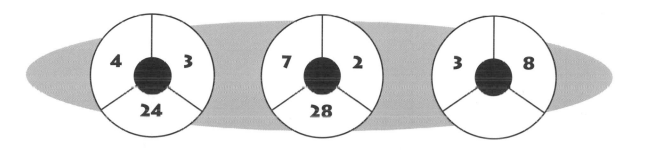

GRID LOCK

Can you work out what numbers are required to complete grids A&B?

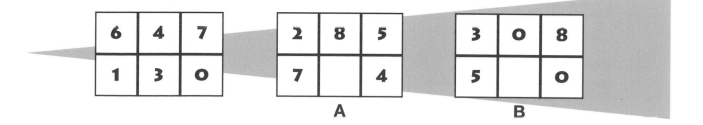

A   B

30

LINES OF THOUGHT

Put on your thinking caps and work out what number is missing from each line of octagons. Use the first line as an example.

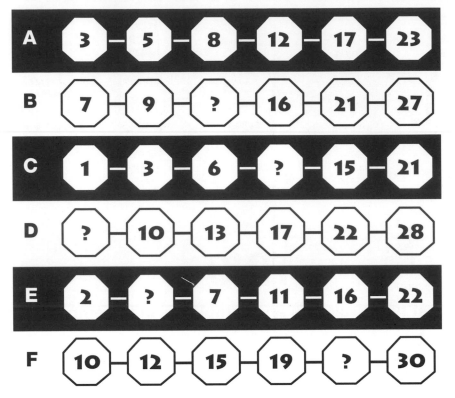

A 3 — 5 — 8 — 12 — 17 — 23

B 7 — 9 — ? — 16 — 21 — 27

C 1 — 3 — 6 — ? — 15 — 21

D ? — 10 — 13 — 17 — 22 — 28

E 2 — ? — 7 — 11 — 16 — 22

F 10 — 12 — 15 — 19 — ? — 30

31

PYRAMID POINTERS

What number goes on the top point of pyramid C?

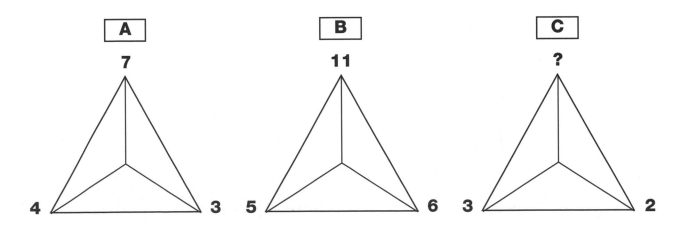

A
7
4   3

B
11
5   6

C
?
3   2

TIME OUT

32

What time should be shown on the blank watch at the end of the top line?

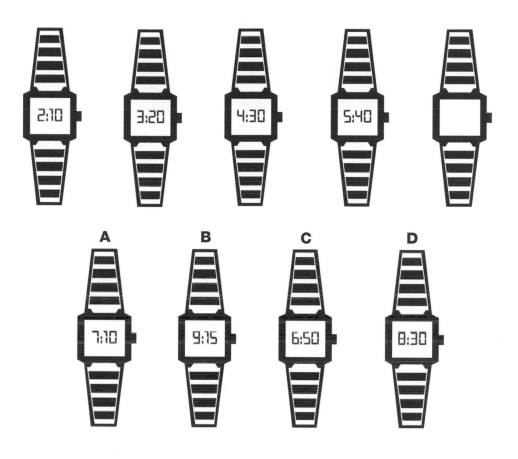

STAR STRUCK

33

Can you complete this puzzle by using the first two stars as a guide?

34

FIGURE—IT—OUT

Complete this puzzle by adding the correct number.
(Clue: Try looking at the puzzle from all directions.)

4	6	2
7	17	10
3	11	?

 35

SLICED UP!

Can you work out what number is missing from the empty segment?
(Clue: Try cutting the circles in half.)

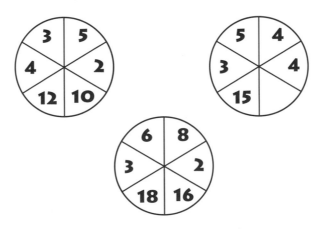

DOTTY DOMINOES!

Which of the six spare dominoes completes this dotty sequence?

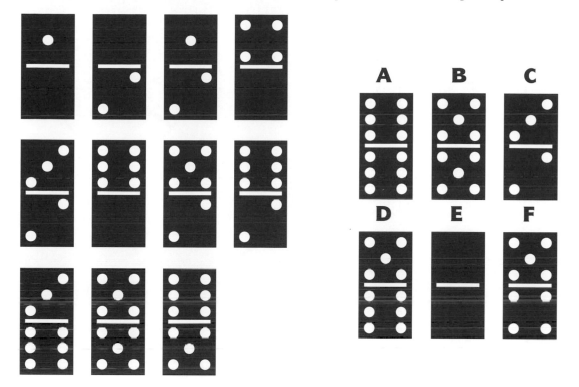

CIRCLES

Fill in the missing number.

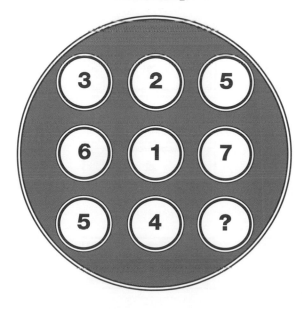

DIGITAL DISCS

38

Using the first two discs as an example, fill in the empty segment.

4 | 6
42

3 | 5

2 | 8
61

BOXING CLEVER

39

Can you work out what number is missing from the empty box?
(Clue: Think square numbers!)

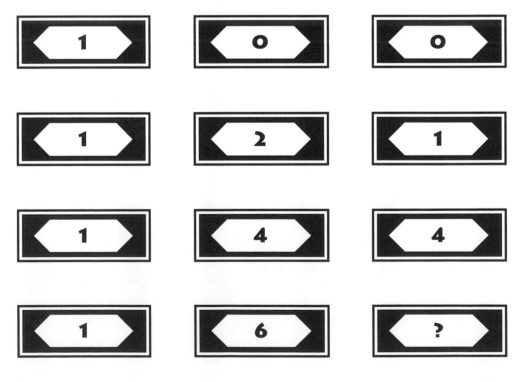

1	0	0
1	2	1
1	4	4
1	6	?

FOUR SQUARE

Fill in the empty shape and complete the puzzle.
(Clue: Look carefully at the grid to find the pattern.)

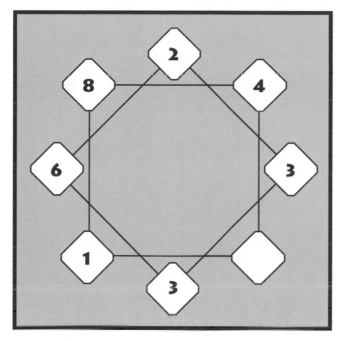

OUT OF PLACE

Which number doesn't go with the rest?

ET CETERA

What number must be added to continue this sequence?

1 2 4 8 16 32 64 ?

NUMBER WHEEL

Replace the question mark in this wheel with the correct number.
(Clue: Look at the numbers in opposite segments.)

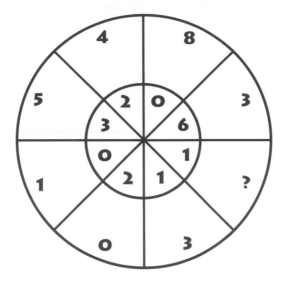

SEQUENTIAL

What number will complete this sequence?

2   4   8   16   ?

HOLE IN ONE

We have left a hole in this puzzle. Can you fill it with the correct number?
(Clue: Don't think in straight lines.)

4   8   12
32   36   16
28   24   ?

MAGIC SQUARE

By using every number between 2 and 10 can you complete this number square so that every line, up and down, left to right, and diagonal adds up to 18?

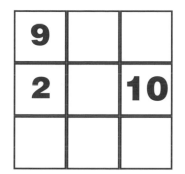

9		
2		10

MISFITS

One number in each square is a misfit, in other words it doesn't follow the same rules or requirements as all the others. Can you work out which one it is?

A

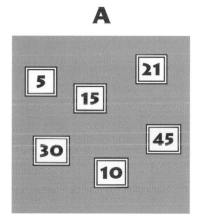

5 21 15 30 45 10

B

18 48 41 36 24 30

C

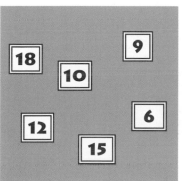

18 9 10 12 6 15

D

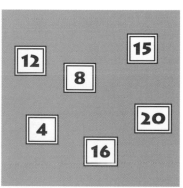

12 15 8 4 20 16

48

FULL HOUSE!

Using the first two houses as an example, can you work out
what number is missing from the third house?

House 1: 12 / 1 2 / 4 2 3

House 2: 17 / 1 3 / 6 5 2

House 3: ? / 2 1 / 7 5 1

49

OPTIONAL EXTRAS

Which of the three optional extra numbers at the bottom will replace the
question mark? (Clue: Don't just look from left to right.)

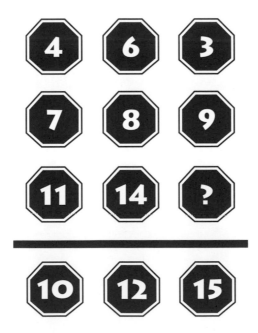

4 6 3

7 8 9

11 14 ?

———

10 12 15

NUMBER SQUARE

50

This puzzle is a little bit different in that we have given you all the numbers already to show you what the finished teaser looks like. Can you work out why these numbers are correct?
(Clue: The center square is the key.)

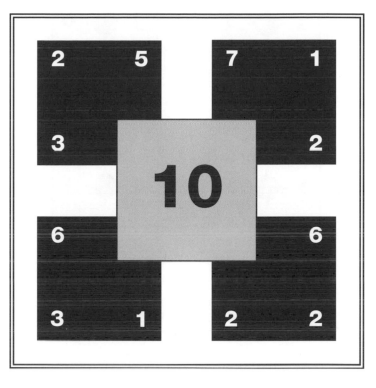

MIND BENDER

51

A stamp dealer bought a rare stamp for $70, sold it for $80, bought it back for $90 and sold it again for $100.

How much money did the stamp dealer make from all this trading?

SQUARE DEAL

Work out what number is missing and complete the puzzle.

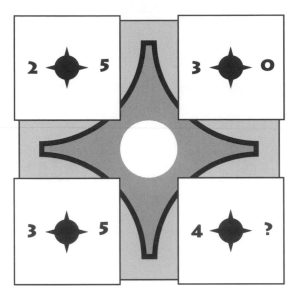

GONE MISSING!

The number in the middle colomn has gone missing. Can you replace it?
(Clue: Look at both sides of the grid.)

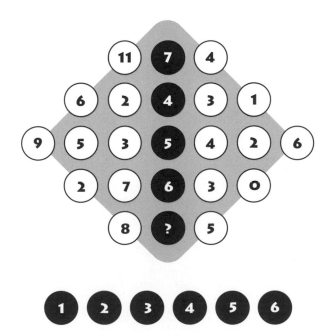

NETWORK

54

Using the first grid as an example, can you complete
grids A and B?

A   B

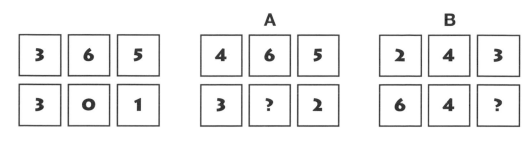

3	6	5
3	0	1

4	6	5
3	?	2

2	4	3
6	4	?

WHEEL SPIN

55

What number is missing from the empty segment in the last wheel?
(Clue: The center wheel in the top row is the link.)

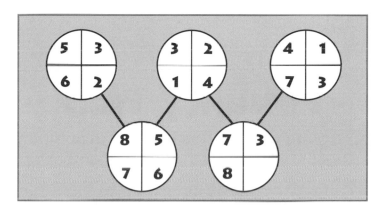

SPACE ODDITY

56

Look at our alien face very carefully and work out which number is the
odd one out in each oval?

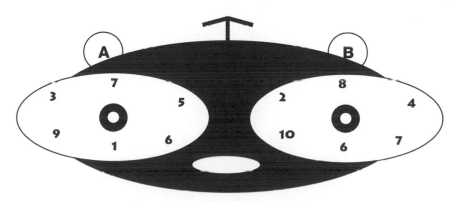

57

RING THE CHANGES

What number goes in the empty ring?

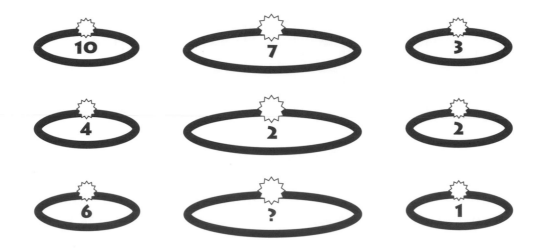

10   7   3

4   2   2

6   ?   1

58

WHACKY WEB

What number do you need to add in order to complete the web?
(Clue: Try looking at opposite numbers.)

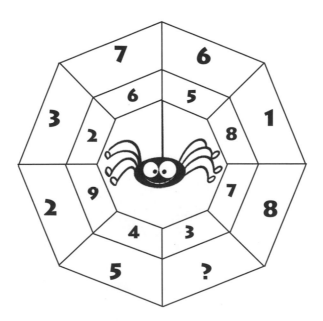

7   6

6   5

3   2   8   1

9   7

2   8

4   3

5   ?

ODD ONE OUT

Which number is the odd one out in each oval?

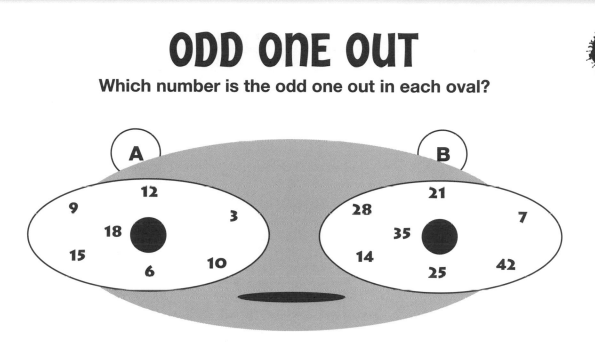

WATCH OUT

Look carefully at the sequence of watches and fill in the blank.

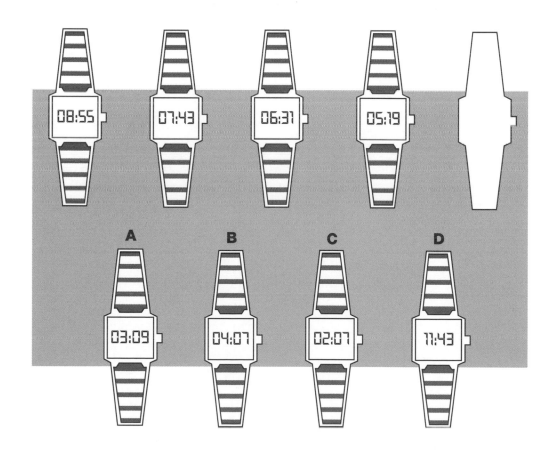

PYRAMID POSER

Work out what number goes at the top of the third pyramid.

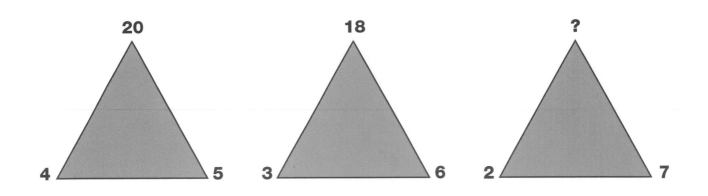

ALL SQUARE

Here is a complete puzzle—work out why it contains these numbers.
(Clue: The center square holds the answer.)

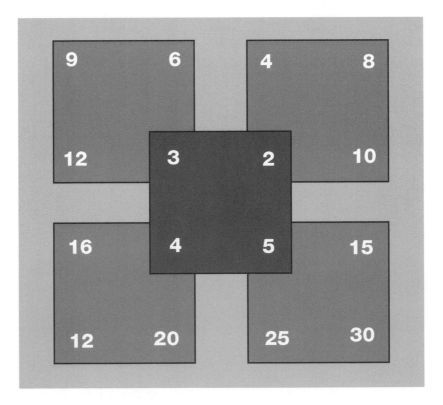

DOTTY DOMINOES

By counting the dots on these dominoes, can you work out which of the six spare pieces completes the sequence?

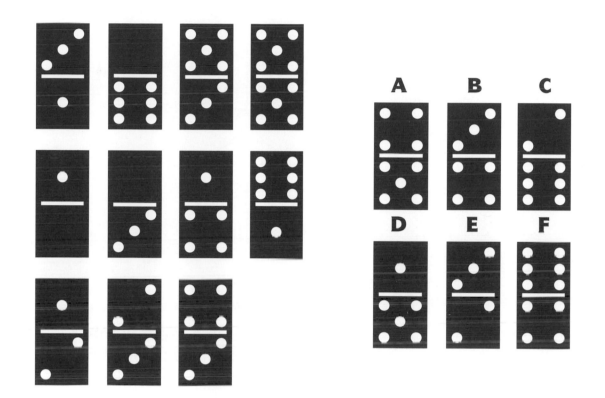

CROSS OVER

What number is missing from each puzzle?

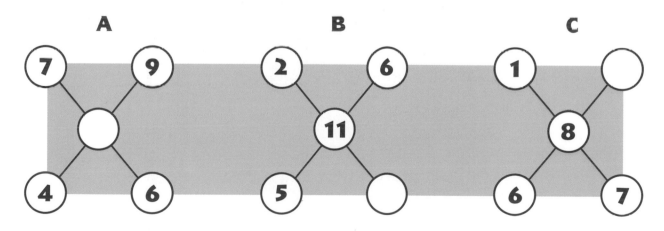

TRI—PIE

What number is missing from the empty segment?
(Clue: Look at the matching segments on each circle.)

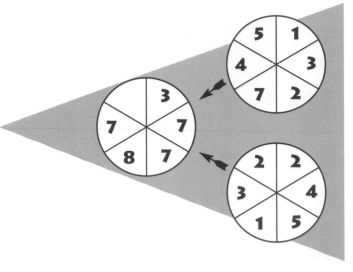

NUMBER BOX

Complete this number box by adding the correct number.
(Clue: The puzzle works up and down as well as side to side!)

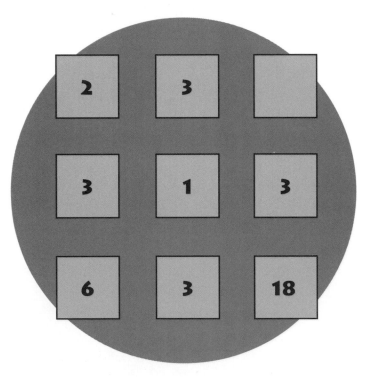

WEB WORLD

What number replaces the question mark and completes the web?
(Clue: Try rotating part of the web.)

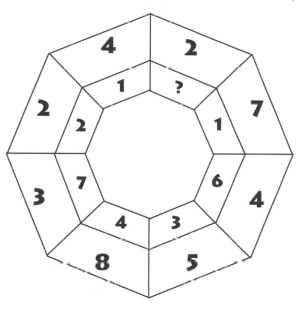

MAGIC SQUARE

Fill in the empty circle and complete the puzzle.
(Clue: Look carefully at the grid to find the pattern.)

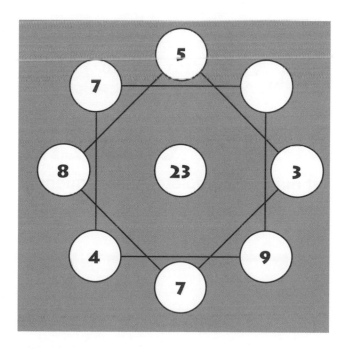

ALL STAR

By using the first two stars as a guide, can you complete this puzzle?
(Clue: Move from point to point).

CIRCLES

What number is needed to finish the puzzle?

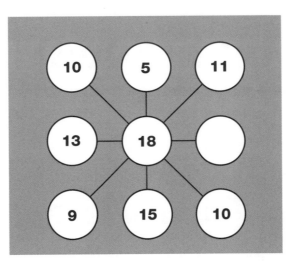

BOXING CLEVER

What number completes this sequence?

2   4   10   28   ?

MISSING NUMBERS

What numbers are missing from the empty grid?
(Clue: Look at the matching segments—the middle circle is the link!)

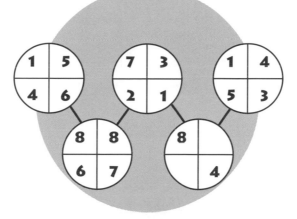

HONEYCOMB

Which number is the odd one out?

HOLE NUMBERS

Complete this puzzle by adding the correct number to the empty circle.
(Clue: Straight thinking will not help you with this one!)

FIGURE—IT—OUT

What three-figure answer is missing from the empty box?

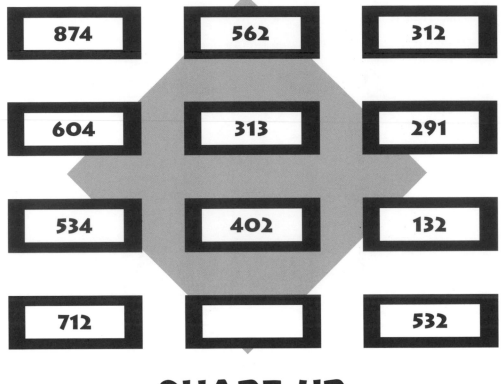

874	562	312
604	313	291
534	402	132
712		532

SHAPE UP

Find the missing number to complete the puzzle.

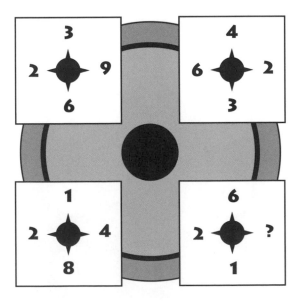

TAKE AWAY

What number goes in the middle oval?
(Clue: It has got nothing to do with sums!)

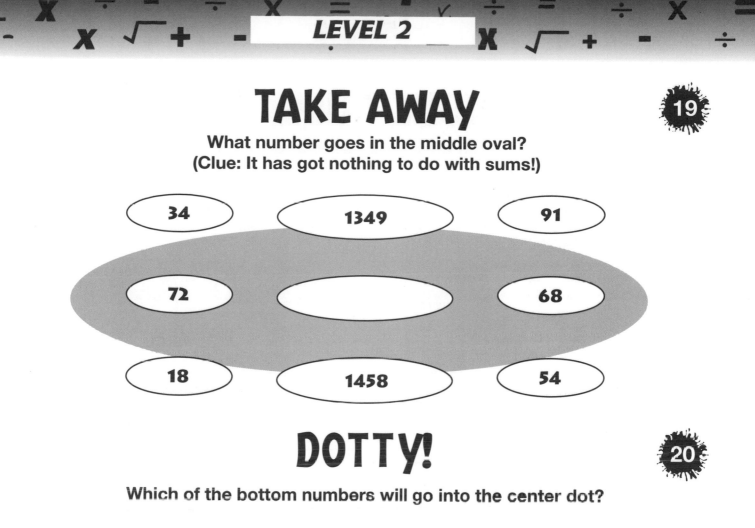

34	1349	91
72		68
18	1458	54

19

DOTTY!

20

Which of the bottom numbers will go into the center dot?

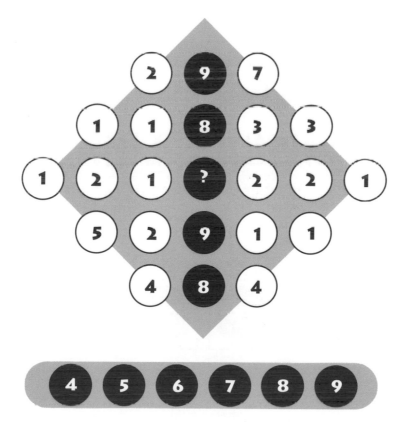

ROGUE NUMBER

In each square we have added a rogue number.
Can you work out which one it is?

A

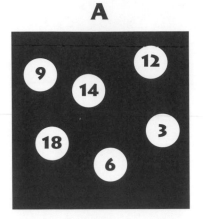

9 12 14 18 3 6

B

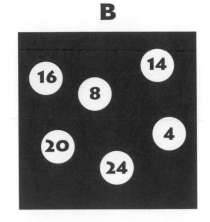

16 14 8 20 4 24

C

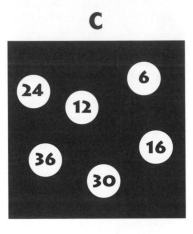

24 6 12 36 16 30

D

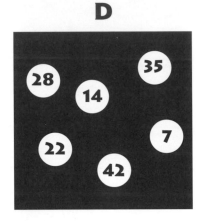

28 35 14 22 7 42

MISSING LINK

What number completes this chain?

3   5   9   15   23   33   45   ?

LINE UP

Using the same rule for every row, can you
fill in the empty octagons?

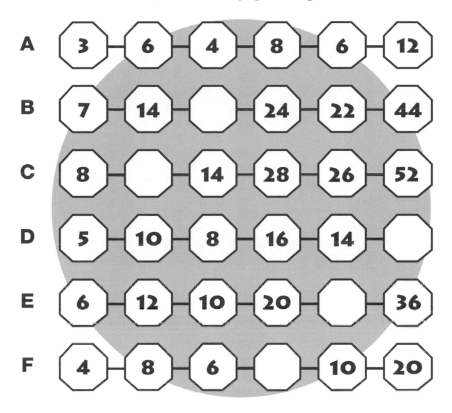

A 3 — 6 — 4 — 8 — 6 — 12

B 7 — 14 — ☐ — 24 — 22 — 44

C 8 — ☐ — 14 — 28 — 26 — 52

D 5 — 10 — 8 — 16 — 14 — ☐

E 6 — 12 — 10 — 20 — ☐ — 36

F 4 — 8 — 6 — ☐ — 10 — 20

CHANGE IT

Replace the question mark with the correct number.
(Clue: Look at the relationship between the numbers in each segment.)

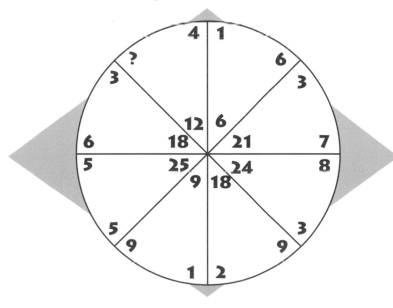

OPTIONS

Which of the three numbers at the bottom will complete this puzzle?
(Clue: Try looking up and down.)

NUMBER SQUARE

By using every number between 1 and 16 can you complete this number square so that every line, up and down, left to right, and diagonal adds up to 34?

13			16
	10	11	
	6		
1			4

STAR STRUCK

27

Using the first two stars as an example, find the missing number.

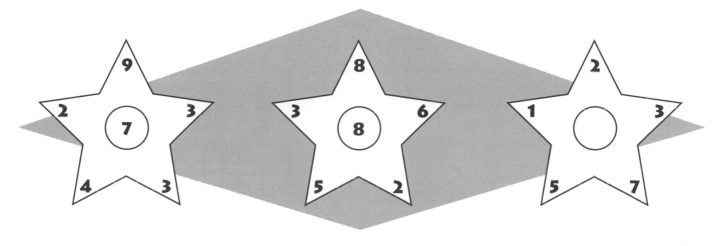

TRIO

28

Using the first two circles as an example, fill in the empty segment.

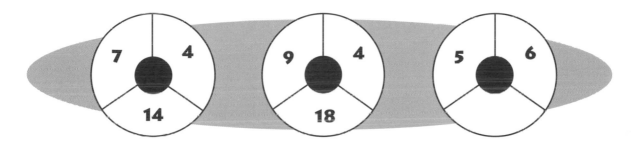

GRID LOCK

29

Can you work out what numbers are required to complete grids A&B?

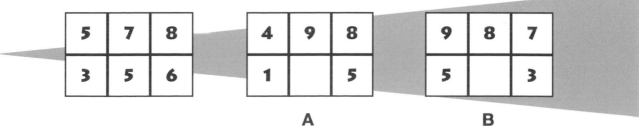

A

B

LINES OF THOUGHT

Put on your thinking caps and work out what number is missing from each line of octagons. Use the first line as an example.

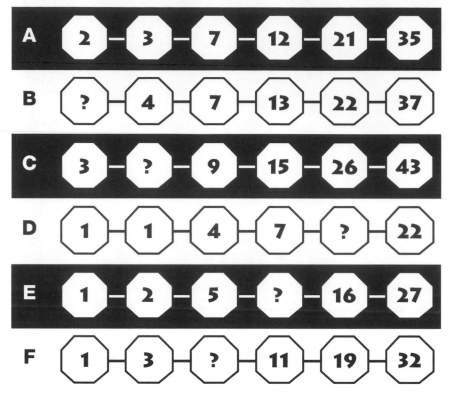

A 2 – 3 – 7 – 12 – 21 – 35

B ? – 4 – 7 – 13 – 22 – 37

C 3 – ? – 9 – 15 – 26 – 43

D 1 – 1 – 4 – 7 – ? – 22

E 1 – 2 – 5 – ? – 16 – 27

F 1 – 3 – ? – 11 – 19 – 32

PYRAMID POINTERS

What number goes on the top point of pyramid C?

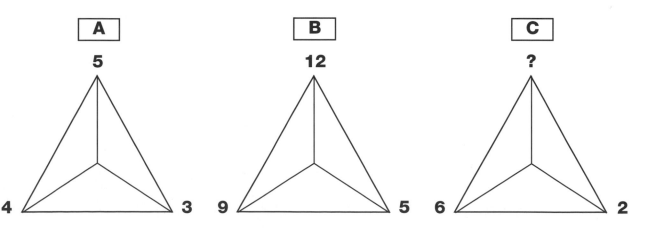

A
5
4   3

B
12
9   5

C
?
6   2

TIME OUT

What time should be shown on the blank watch at the end of the top line?

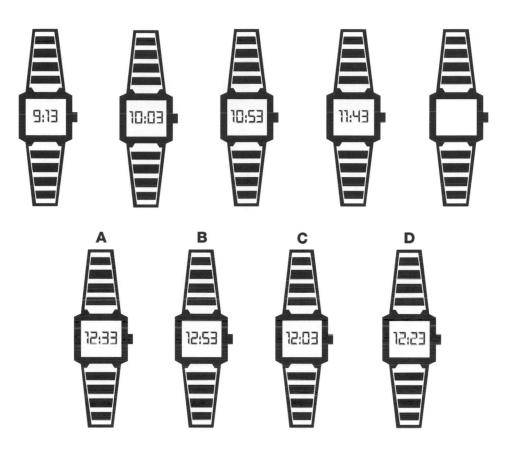

9:13 10:03 10:53 11:43 [blank]

A 12:33   **B** 12:53   **C** 12:03   **D** 12:23

STAR STRUCK

Can you complete this puzzle by using the first two stars as a guide?

Star 1: 2, 13, 3, 8, 5

Star 2: 1, 8, 2, 5, 3

Star 3: 3, 18, 4, 11, ?

FIGURE IT OUT

Complete this puzzle by adding the correct number.
(Clue: Try looking at the puzzle from all directions.)

SLICED UP!

Can you work out what number is missing from the empty segment?
(Clue: Look at matching segments.)

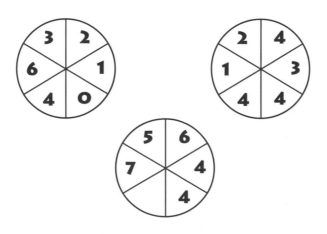

DOTTY DOMINOES!

Which of the six spare dominoes completes this dotty sequence?

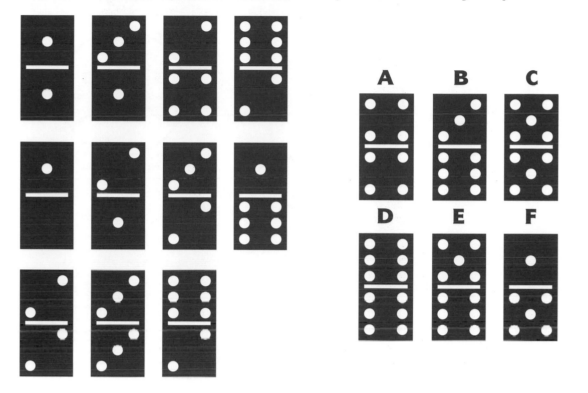

CIRCLES

Fill in the missing number.

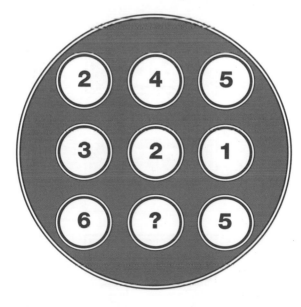

DIGITAL DISCS

38

Using the first two discs as an example, fill in the empty segment.

BOXING CLEVER

39

Can you work out what number is missing from the empty box?
(Clue: You might need a calculator for this one!)

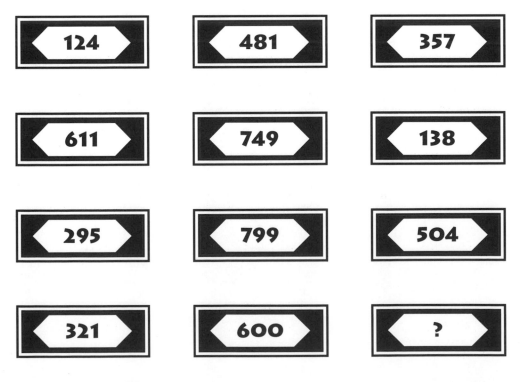

FOUR SQUARE

Fill in the empty shape and complete the puzzle.
(Clue: Look carefully at the grid to find the pattern.)

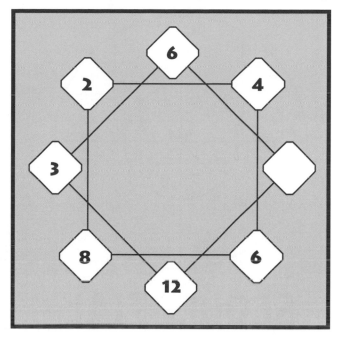

OUT OF PLACE

Which number doesn't go with the rest?

ET CETERA

What number must be added to continue this sequence?

NUMBER WHEEL

Replace the question mark in this wheel with the correct number.
(Clue: Look at the numbers in each segment as a group.)

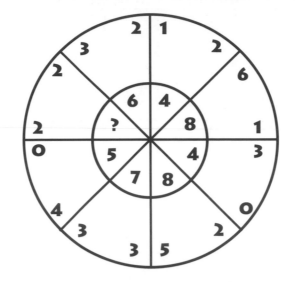

SEQUENTIAL

What number will complete this sequence?

HOLE IN ONE

We have left a hole in this puzzle. Can you fill it with the correct number?
(Clue: Don't think in straight lines.)

MAGIC SQUARE

By using every number between 1 and 16 can you complete this number square so that every line, up and down, left to right, and diagonal adds up to 34?

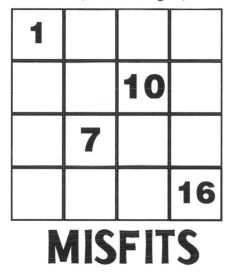

MISFITS

One number in each square is a misfit, in other words it doesn't follow the same rules or requirements as all the others. Can you work out which one it is?

A

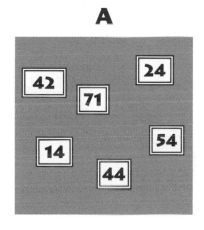

B

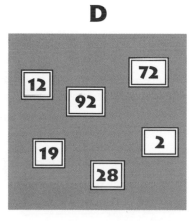

C

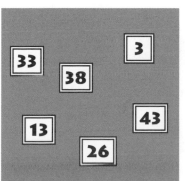

D

FULL HOUSE!

Using the first two houses as an example, can you work out
what number is missing from the third house?

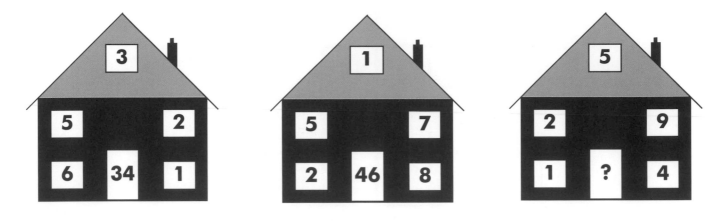

3

5   2

6   34   1

1

5   7

2   46   8

5

2   9

1   ?   4

OPTIONAL EXTRAS

Which of the three optional extra numbers at the bottom will replace the
question mark? (Clue: Don't just look from left to right.)

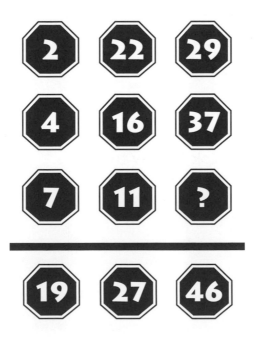

2   22   29

4   16   37

7   11   ?

19   27   46

NUMBER SQUARE

This puzzle is a little bit different in that we have given you all the numbers already to show you what the finished teaser looks like. Can you work out why these numbers are correct?
(Clue: The center square is the key.)

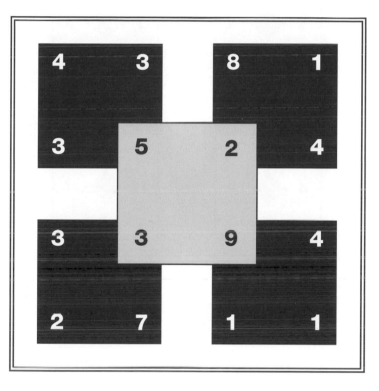

MIND BENDER

Jack and Martha have been married for 20 years. If you add Jack's age to Martha's, you get a combined age of 91 years. Jack is now twice as old as Martha was when he was as old as she is now. From this information, can you work out how old Jack and Martha are now?

SQUARE DEAL

Work out what number is missing and complete the puzzle.

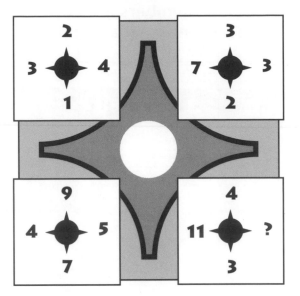

GONE MISSING!

The number in the middle column has gone missing, can you replace it?
(Clue: Look at both sides of the grid.)

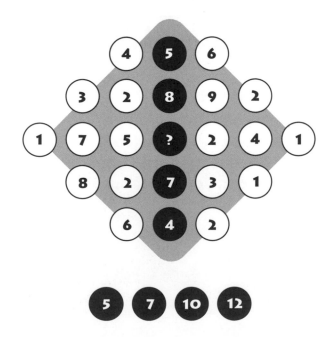

NETWORK

Using the first grid as an example, can you complete grids A and B?

54

12	18	24
30	36	42

A

14	21	28
?	42	49

B

16	24	32
40	48	?

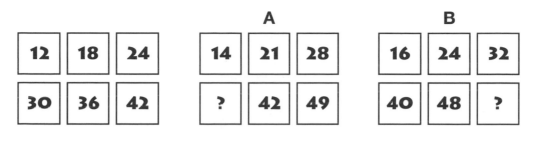

WHEEL SPIN

55

What numbers are missing from the lower right circle?

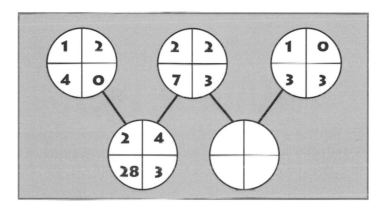

SPACE ODDITY

56

Look at our alien face very carefully and work out which number is the odd one out in each oval?

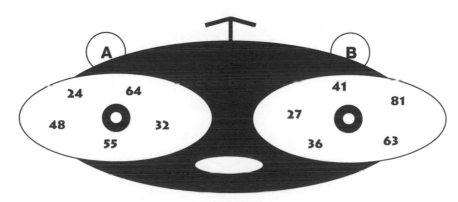

RING THE CHANGES

What number goes in the empty ring?

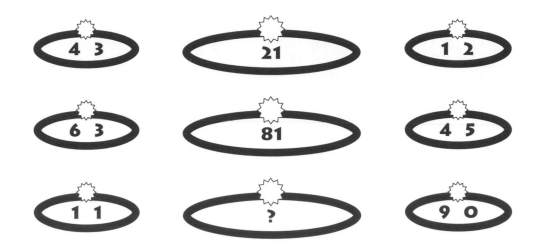

WHACKY WEB

What number do you need to add in order to complete the web?
(Clue: Try rotating the outer segments.)

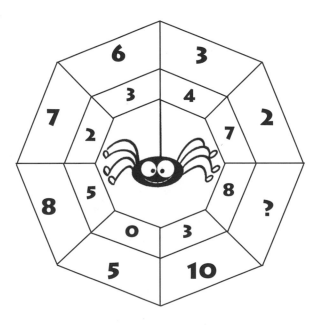

ODD ONE OUT

1

Which number is the odd one out in each oval?

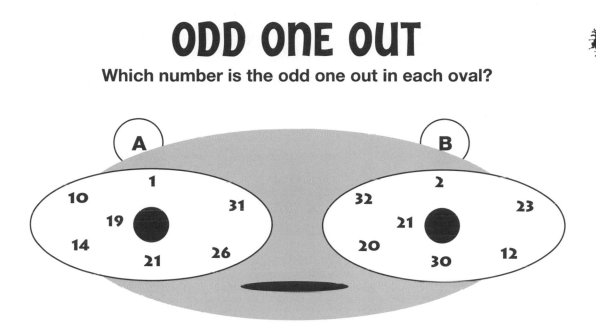

WATCH OUT

2

Look carefully at the sequence of watches and fill in the blank.

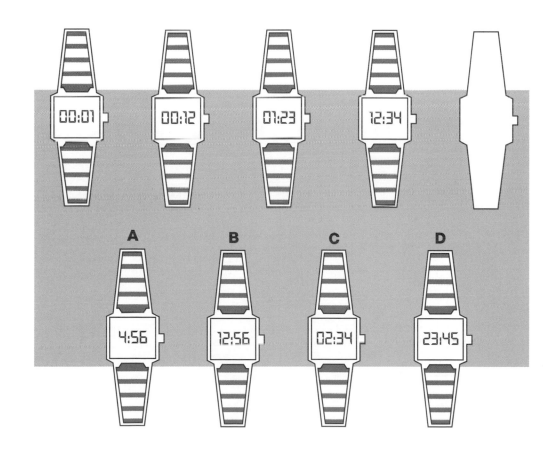

3 PYRAMID POSER

Work out what number goes at the top of the third pyramid?

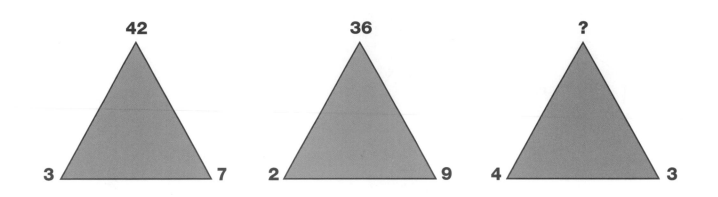

42

36

?

3   7

2   9

4   3

4 ALL SQUARE

Here is a complete puzzle—work out why it contains these numbers.
(Clue: The center square holds the answer.)

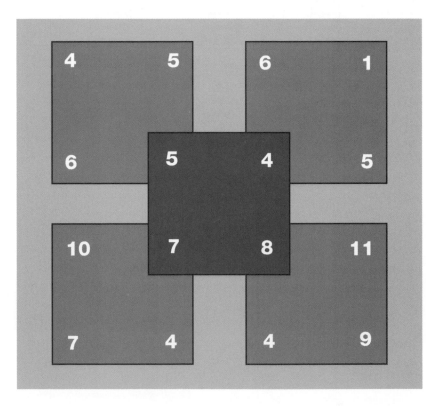

DOTTY DOMINOES

5

By counting the dots on these dominoes, can you work out which of the six spare pieces completes the sequence?

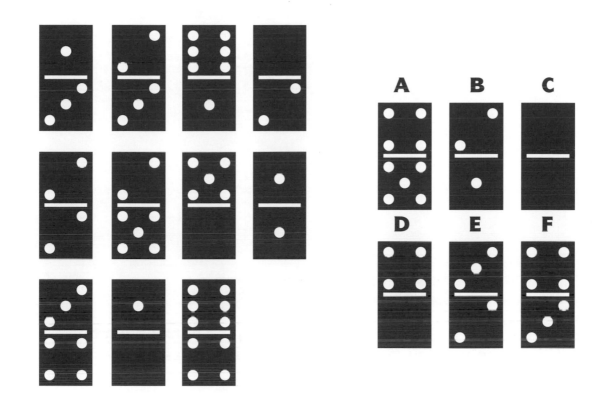

A B C
D E F

CROSS OVER

6

What number is missing from each puzzle?

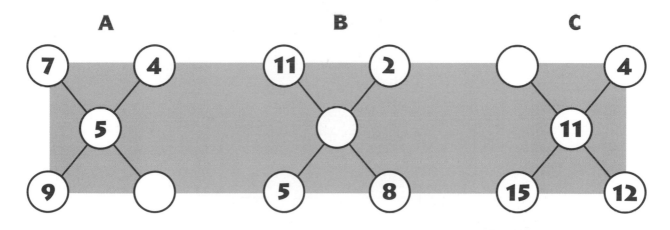

TRI—PIE

What number is missing from the empty segment?
(Clue: Look at the matching segments on each circle.)

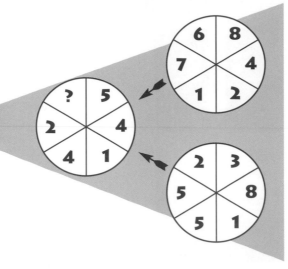

NUMBER BOX

Complete this number box by adding the correct number.
(Clue: The puzzle works up and down as well as side to side!)

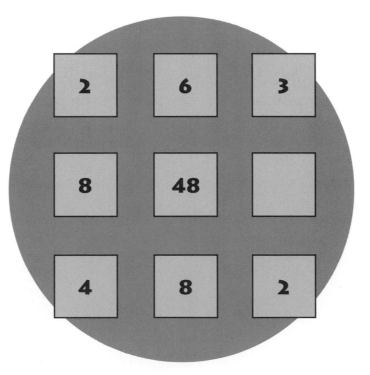

WEB WORLD

What number replaces the question mark
and completes the web?

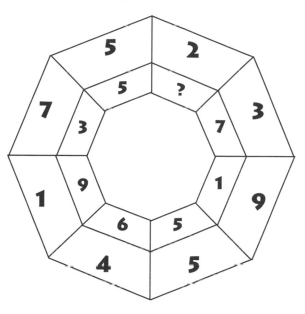

MAGIC SQUARE

Fill in the empty circle and complete the puzzle.
(Clue: Look carefully at the grid to find the pattern.)

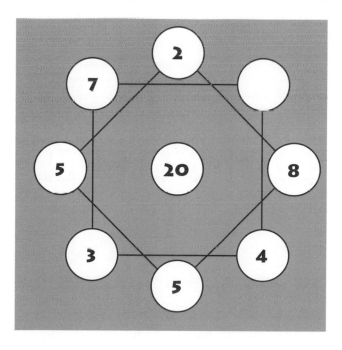

ALL STAR

By using the first two stars as a guide, can you complete this puzzle?

CIRCLES

What number is needed to finish the puzzle?

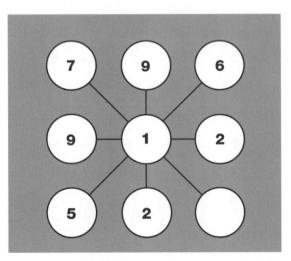

BOXING CLEVER

What number completes this sequence?

MISSING NUMBERS

What numbers are missing from the empty grid?
(Clue: Look at the matching segments—the middle circle is the link!)

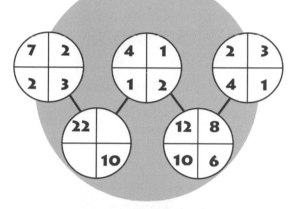

HONEYCOMB

Which number is the odd one out?

HOLE NUMBERS

Complete this puzzle by adding the correct number to the empty circle.
(Clue: Straight thinking will not help you with this one!)

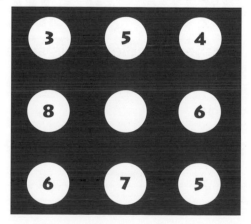

FIGURE—IT—OUT

What four-figure answer is missing from the empty box?

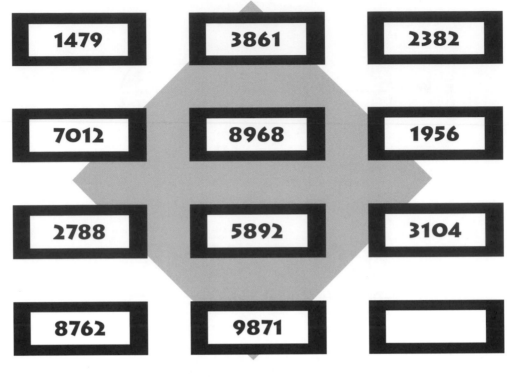

1479	3861	2382
7012	8968	1956
2788	5892	3104
8762	9871	

SHAPE UP

Find the missing number to complete the puzzle.

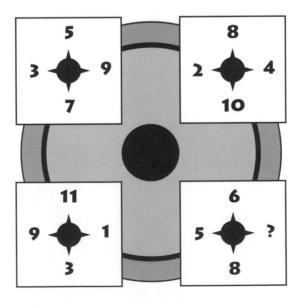

TAKE AWAY

19

What number goes in the middle oval?
(Clue: It has got nothing to do with sums!)

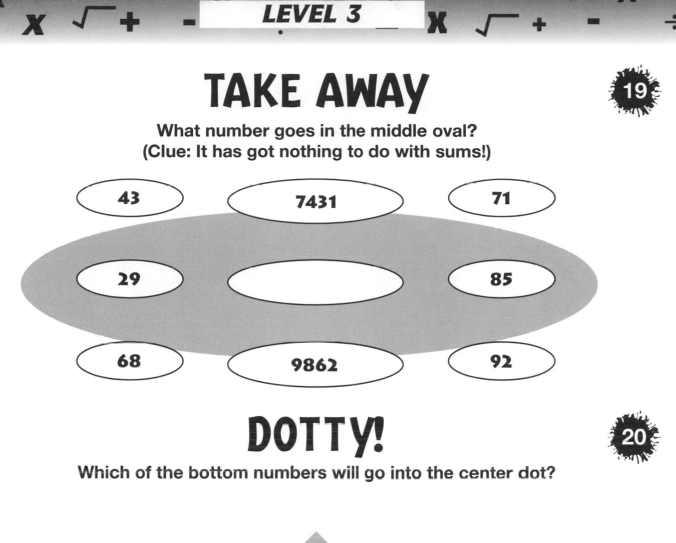

43   7431   71

29   85

68   9862   92

DOTTY!

20

Which of the bottom numbers will go into the center dot?

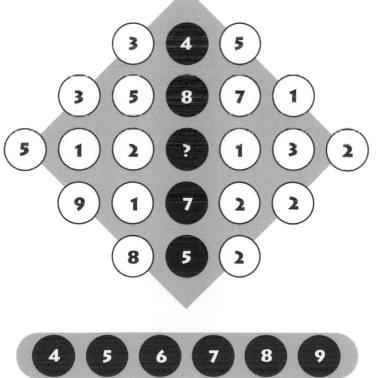

ROGUE NUMBER

In each square we have added a rogue number.
Can you work out which one it is?

A

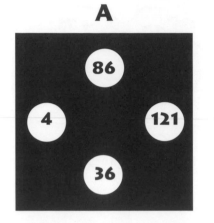

86
4
121
36

B

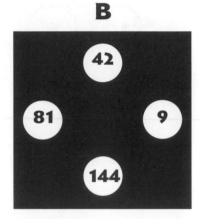

42
81
9
144

C

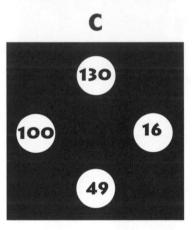

130
100
16
49

D

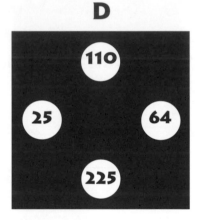

110
25
64
225

MISSING LINK

What number completes this chain?

5   7   6   8   7   9   8   ?

LINE UP

Using the same rule for every row, can you
fill in the empty octagons?

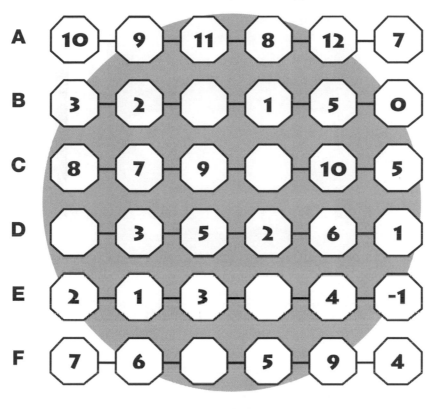

A: 10 – 9 – 11 – 8 – 12 – 7

B: 3 – 2 – ☐ – 1 – 5 – 0

C: 8 – 7 – 9 – ☐ – 10 – 5

D: ☐ – 3 – 5 – 2 – 6 – 1

E: 2 – 1 – 3 – ☐ – 4 – -1

F: 7 – 6 – ☐ – 5 – 9 – 4

CHANGE IT

Replace the question mark with the correct number.
(Clue: Look at the relationship between the numbers in each segment.)

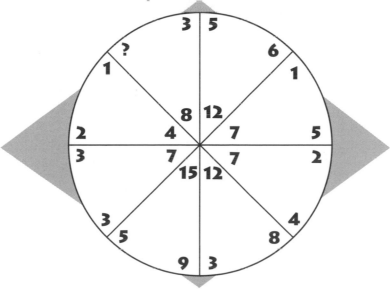

OPTIONS

Which of the three numbers at the bottom will complete this puzzle?
(Clue: Try looking up and down.)

5	13	11
9		15
7	11	13

8   9   10

NUMBER SQUARE

By using every number between 1 and 16 can you complete this number square
so that every line, up and down, left to right, and diagonal adds up to 34?

7		9	
		3	
4			11
	15		1

STAR STRUCK

Using the first two stars as an example, find the missing number.

TRIO

Using the first two circles as an example, fill in the empty segment.

GRID LOCK

Can you work out what numbers are required to complete grids A and B?

2	9	7
4	81	49

6	3	8
36		64

A

1	5	4
1		16

B

LINES OF THOUGHT

Put on your thinking caps and work out what number is missing from each line of octagons. Use the first line as an example.

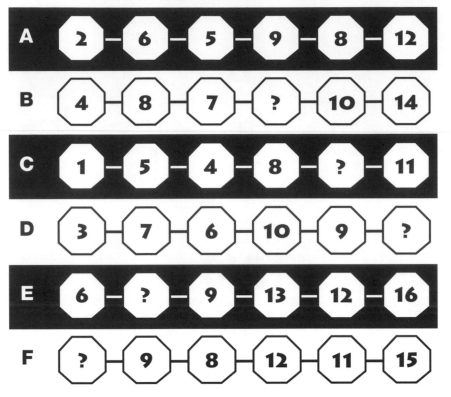

A 2 — 6 — 5 — 9 — 8 — 12

B 4 — 8 — 7 — ? — 10 — 14

C 1 — 5 — 4 — 8 — ? — 11

D 3 — 7 — 6 — 10 — 9 — ?

E 6 — ? — 9 — 13 — 12 — 16

F ? — 9 — 8 — 12 — 11 — 15

PYRAMID POINTERS

What number goes on the top point of pyramid C?

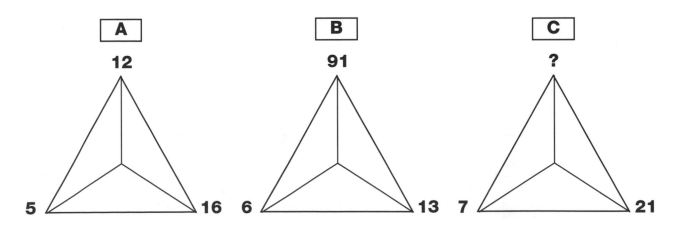

A	B	C
12	91	?
5 16	6 13	7 21

TIME OUT

What time should be shown on the blank watch at the end of the top line?

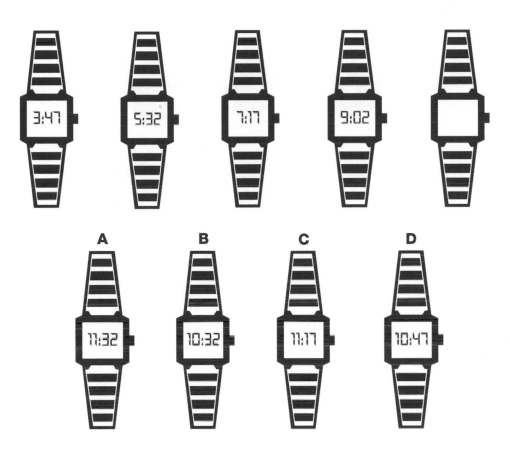

3:47 5:32 7:17 9:02

A 11:32 B 10:32 C 11:17 D 10:47

STAR STRUCK

Can you complete this puzzle?
(Clue: The lower two digits in each star are not what they seem.)

16 11 4 3 1

9 17 13 3 9

10 15 10 3 ?

FIGURE IT OUT

Complete this puzzle by adding the correct number.
(Clue: Try looking at the puzzle from all directions.)

 # SLICED UP!

Can you work out what number is missing from the empty segment?
(Clue: Look at matching segments.)

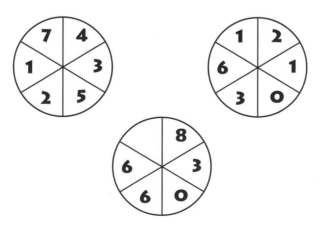

DOTTY DOMINOES!

Which of the six spare dominoes completes this dotty sequence?

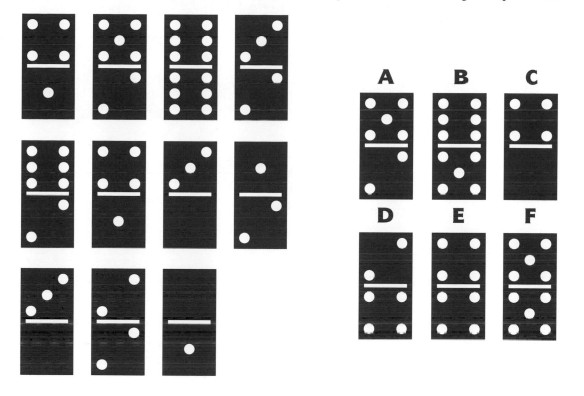

CIRCLES

Fill in the missing number.

DIGITAL DISCS

Using the first two discs as an example, fill in the empty segment.

BOXING CLEVER

Can you work out what number is missing from the empty box?
(Clue: Look at each column separately.)

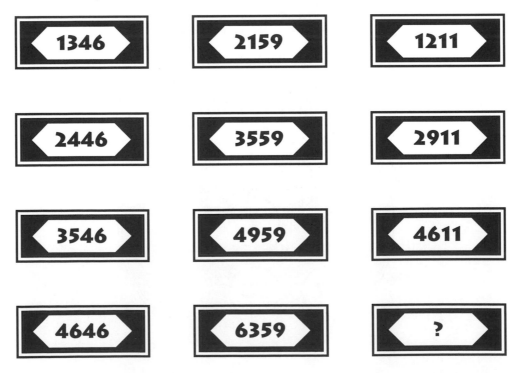

1346	2159	1211
2446	3559	2911
3546	4959	4611
4646	6359	?

FOUR SQUARE

Fill in the empty shape and complete the puzzle.
(Clue: Look carefully at the grid to find the pattern.)

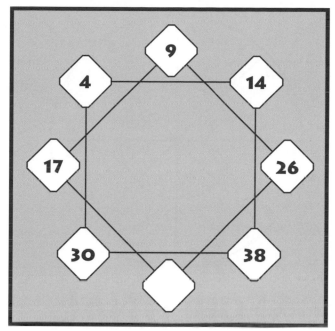

OUT OF PLACE

Which number doesn't go with the rest?

ET CETERA

What number must be added to continue this sequence?

NUMBER WHEEL

Replace the question mark in this wheel with the correct number.
(Clue: Look at the numbers in each segment as a group.)

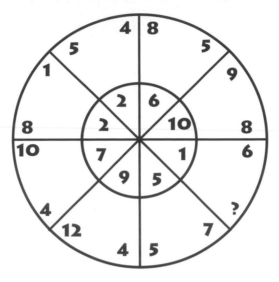

SEQUENTIAL

What number will complete this sequence?

3   7   15   31   ?

HOLE IN ONE

We have left a hole in this puzzle. Can you fill it with the correct number?
(Clue: Don't think in straight lines.)

MAGIC SQUARE

By using every number between 1 and 16 can you complete this number square so that every line, up and down, left to right, and diagonal adds up to 34?

MISFITS

One number in each square is a misfit, in other words it doesn't follow the same rules or requirements as all the others. Can you work out which one it is?

A

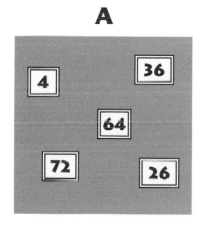

B

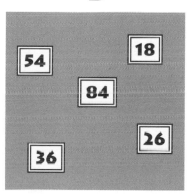

C

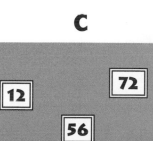

D

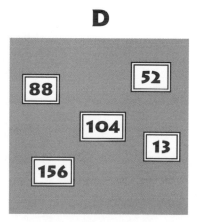

FULL HOUSE!

Using the first two houses as an example, can you work out which number is missing from the third house?

OPTIONAL EXTRAS

Which of the three optional extra numbers at the bottom will replace the question mark? (Clue: Don't just look from left to right.)

NUMBER SQUARE

This puzzle is a little bit different in that we have given you all the numbers already to show you what the finished teaser looks like. Can you work out why these numbers are correct?
(Clue: The center square is the key.)

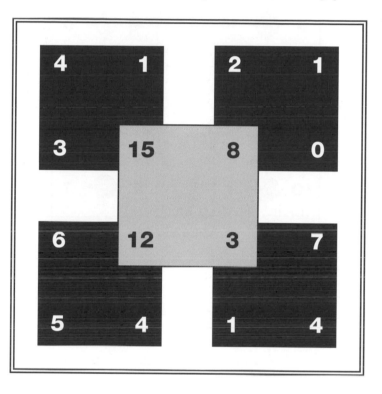

MIND BENDER

The Bingly Drive Neighborhood Watch group meet every month to catch up with the latest news. At today's meeting, as with every other, each member of the group shakes hands exactly once with every other person present. In total, there were 45 handshakes.

Can you calculate how many people were present at the meeting?

SQUARE DEAL

Work out what number is missing and complete the puzzle.

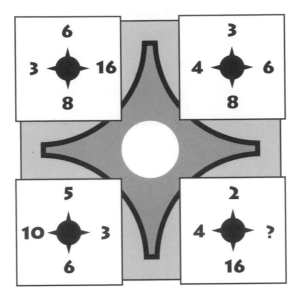

GONE MISSING!

The number in the middle column has gone missing, can you replace it?

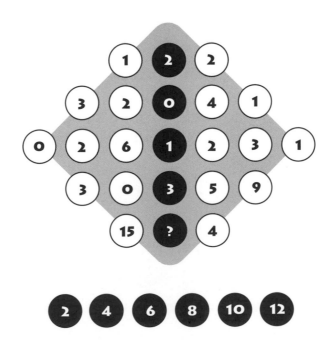

NETWORK

Using the first grid as an example, can you complete grids A and B?

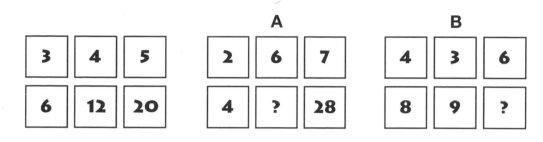

A   B

3	4	5		2	6	7		4	3	6
6	12	20		4	?	28		8	9	?

WHEEL SPIN

What numbers are missing from the last wheel?
(Clue: Move up and down to get the answer.)

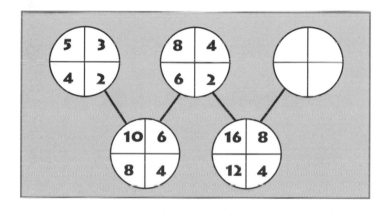

SPACE ODDITY

Look at our alien face very carefully and work out which number is the odd one out in each oval?

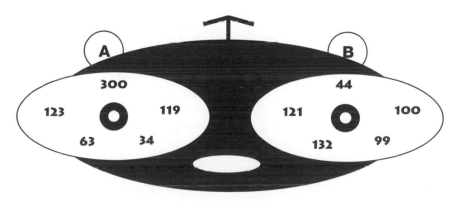

57

RING THE CHANGES
What number goes in the empty ring?

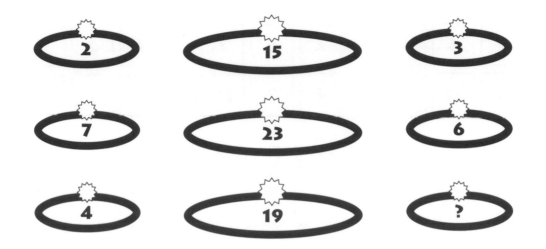

2	15	3
7	23	6
4	19	?

58

WHACKY WEB
What number do you need to add in order to complete the web?

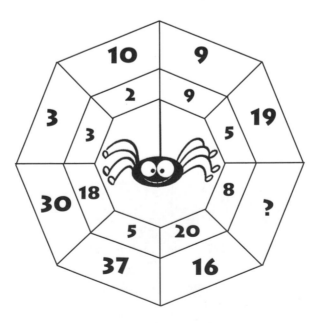

10 9
2 9
3
3
19
5
30 18
8
?
5 20
37 16

ODD ONE OUT

1

Which number is the odd one out in each oval?

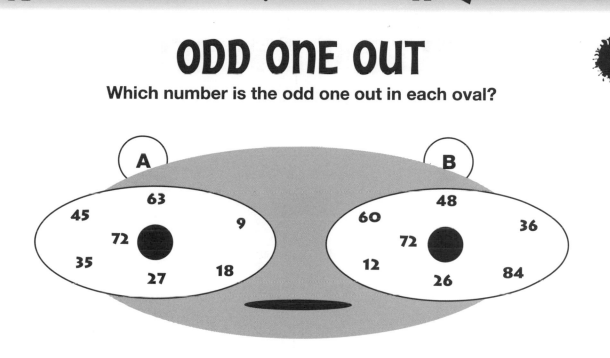

WATCH OUT

2

Look carefully at the sequence of watches and fill in the blank.

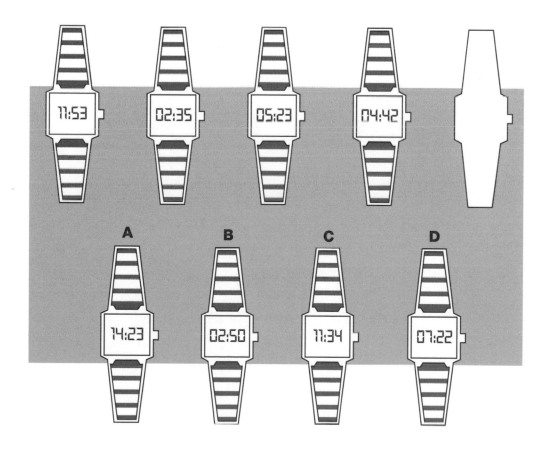

3

PYRAMID POSER

Work out what number goes at the top of the third pyramid?

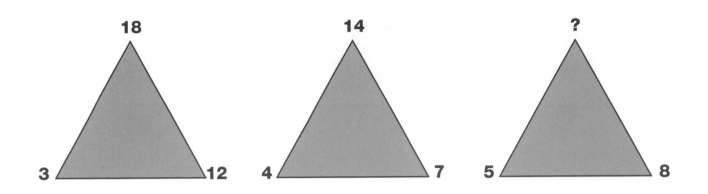

18

3   12

14

4   7

?

5   8

 4

ALL SQUARE

Here is a complete puzzle—work out why it contains these numbers.
(Clue: The center square holds the answer.)

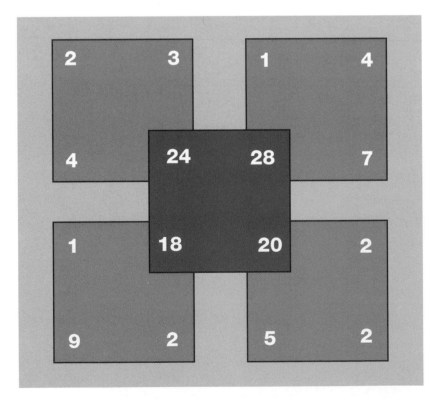

DOTTY DOMINOES

By counting the dots on these dominoes, can you work out
which of the six spare pieces completes the sequence?

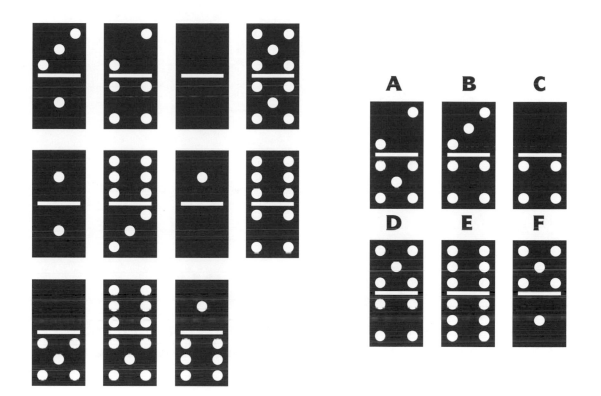

CROSS OVER

What number is missing from each puzzle?

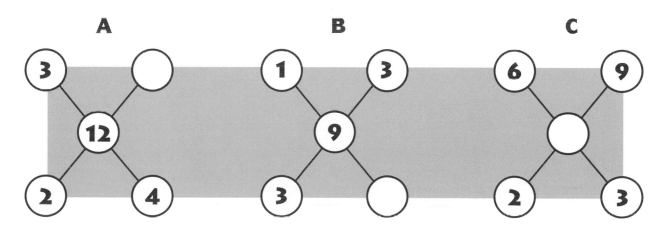

TRI–PIE

What number is missing from the empty segment?
(Clue: Look at the matching segments on each circle.)

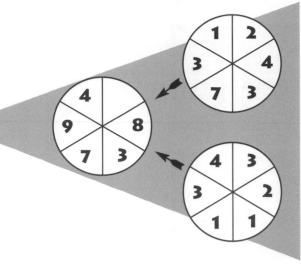

NUMBER BOX

Complete this number box by adding the correct number.
(Clue: The puzzle works up and down as well as side to side!)

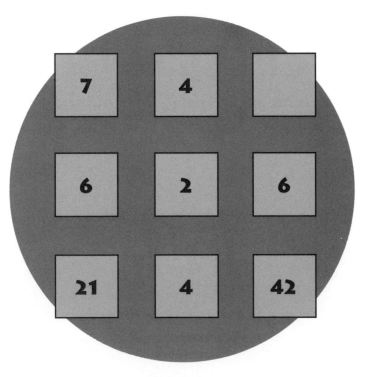

WEB WORLD

What number replaces the question mark and completes the web?

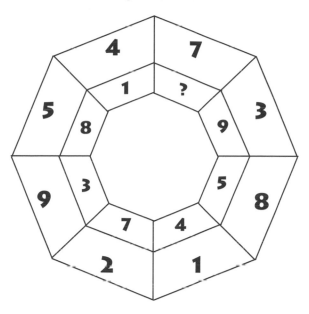

MAGIC SQUARE

Fill in the empty circle and complete the puzzle.
(Clue: Look carefully at the grid to find the pattern.)

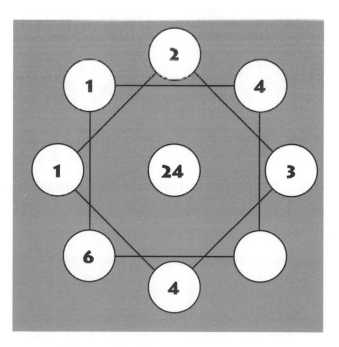

11 ALL STAR

By using the first two stars as a guide, can you complete this puzzle?

12 CIRCLES

What number is needed to finish the puzzle?

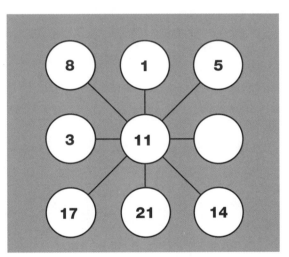

13 BOXING CLEVER

What number completes this sequence?

1   8   22   50   ?

MISSING NUMBERS

What numbers are missing from the empty grid?
(Clue: Look at the matching segments—the middle circle is the link!)

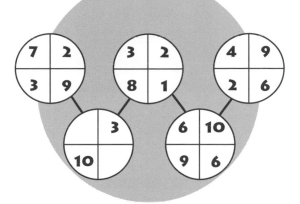

HONEYCOMB

Which number is the odd one out?

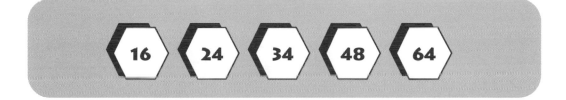

HOLE NUMBERS

Complete this puzzle by adding the correct number to the empty circle.
(Clue: Straight thinking will not help you with this one!)

FIGURE—IT—OUT

What four-figure answer is missing from the empty box?

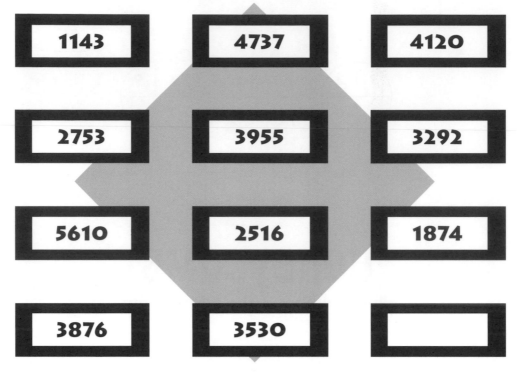

1143	4737	4120
2753	3955	3292
5610	2516	1874
3876	3530	

SHAPE UP

Find the missing number to complete the puzzle.

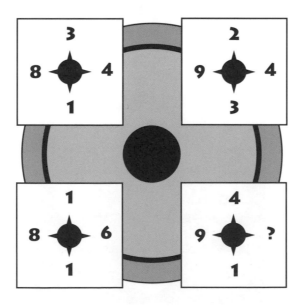

TAKE AWAY

19

What number goes in the middle oval?
(Clue: It has got nothing to do with sums!)

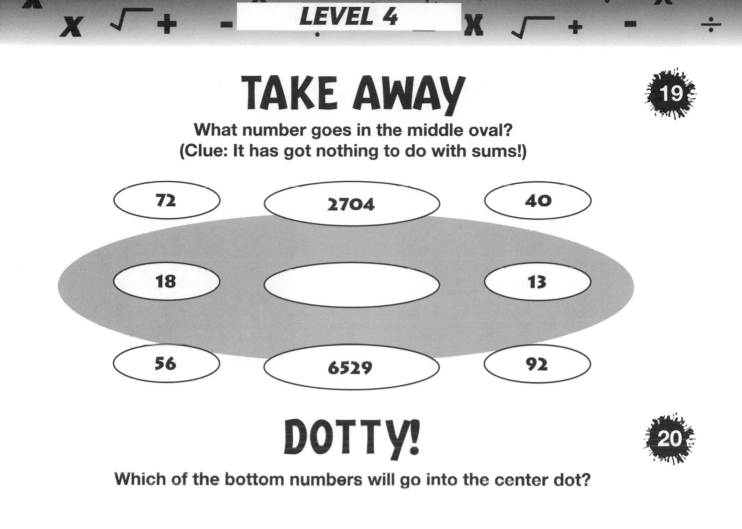

72	2704	40
18		13
56	6529	92

DOTTY!

20

Which of the bottom numbers will go into the center dot?

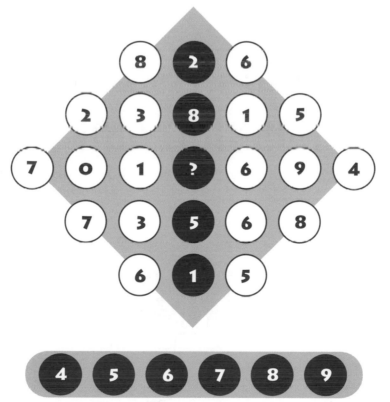

21

ROGUE NUMBER

In each square we have added a rogue number.
Can you work out which one it is?

A

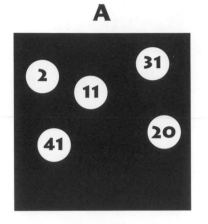

B

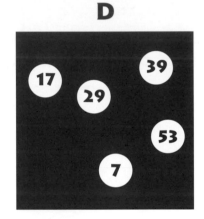

C

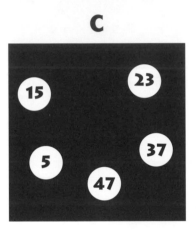

D

22

MISSING LINK

What number completes this chain?

LINE UP

Using the same rule for every row, can you
fill in the empty octagons?

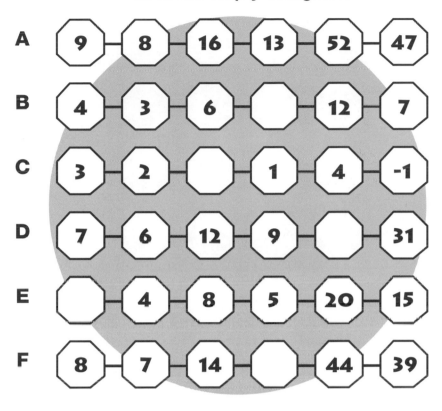

A 9 — 8 — 16 — 13 — 52 — 47

B 4 — 3 — 6 — ◯ — 12 — 7

C 3 — 2 — ◯ — 1 — 4 — -1

D 7 — 6 — 12 — 9 — ◯ — 31

E ◯ — 4 — 8 — 5 — 20 — 15

F 8 — 7 — 14 — ◯ — 44 — 39

CHANGE IT

Replace the question mark with the correct number.
(Clue: Look at the relationship between the numbers in each segment.)

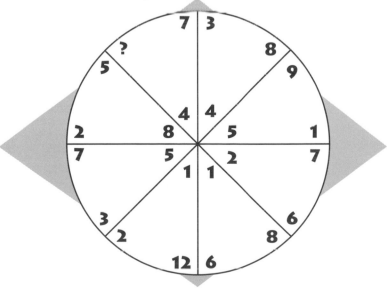

OPTIONS

Which of the three numbers at the bottom will complete this puzzle?
(Clue: Try looking up and down.)

NUMBER SQUARE

By using every number between 1 and 25 can you complete this number square so that every line, up and down, left to right, and diagonal adds up to 65?

			22	25
	18		12	10
23		13		
1	24			21

STAR STRUCK

Using the first two stars as an example, find the missing number.

TRIO

Using the first two circles as an example, fill in the empty segment.

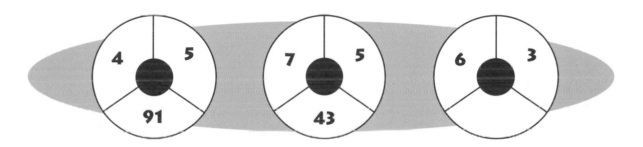

GRID LOCK

Can you work out what numbers are required to complete grids A and B?

23	38	16
48	22	16
17	15	14

37	24	16
18	53	17
19		15

A

16	23	12
37	42	16
17		10

B

30 LINES OF THOUGHT

Put on your thinking caps and work out what number is missing from each line of octagons. Use the first line as an example.

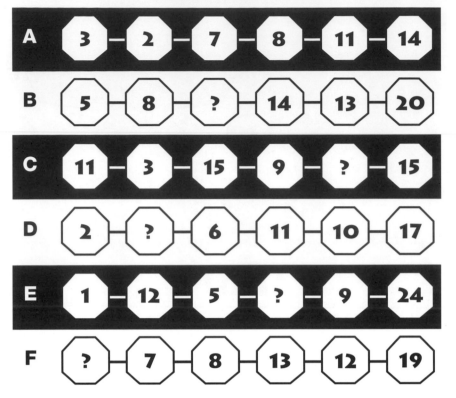

A 3 — 2 — 7 — 8 — 11 — 14

B 5 — 8 — ? — 14 — 13 — 20

C 11 — 3 — 15 — 9 — ? — 15

D 2 — ? — 6 — 11 — 10 — 17

E 1 — 12 — 5 — ? — 9 — 24

F ? — 7 — 8 — 13 — 12 — 19

31 PYRAMID POINTERS

What number goes on the top point of pyramid C?

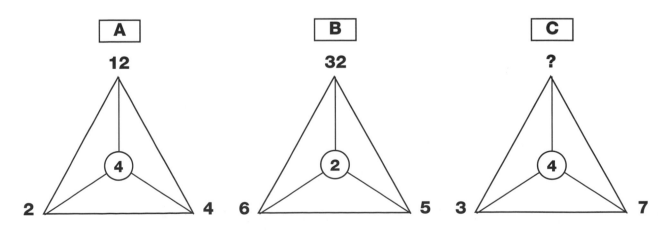

A
12
4
2   4

B
32
2
6   5

C
?
4
3   7

TIME OUT

 32

What time should be shown on the blank watch at the end of the top line?

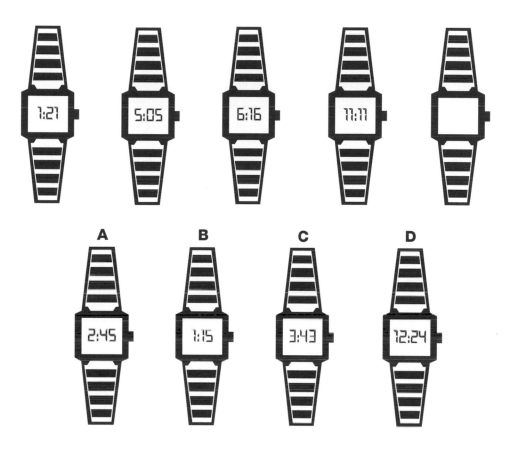

7:21 5:05 6:16 11:11

A B C D

2:45 1:15 3:43 12:24

STAR STRUCK

 33

Can you complete this puzzle by using the first two stars as a guide?

5
20   6
12   8

6
36   8
20   12

7
52   10
?   16

34

FIGURE IT OUT

Complete this puzzle by adding the correct number.
(Clue: Try looking at the puzzle from all directions.)

35

SLICED UP!

Can you work out what number is missing from the empty segment?
(Clue: Look at matching segments.)

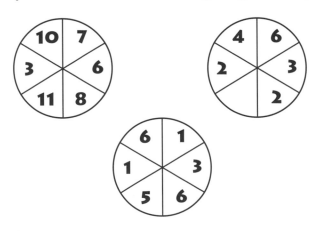

DOTTY DOMINOES!

Which of the six spare dominoes completes this dotty sequence?

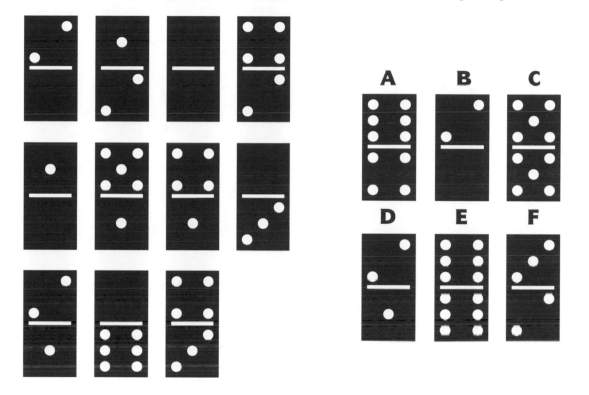

CIRCLES

Fill in the missing number.

DIGITAL DISCS

38

Using the first two discs as an example, fill in the empty segment.

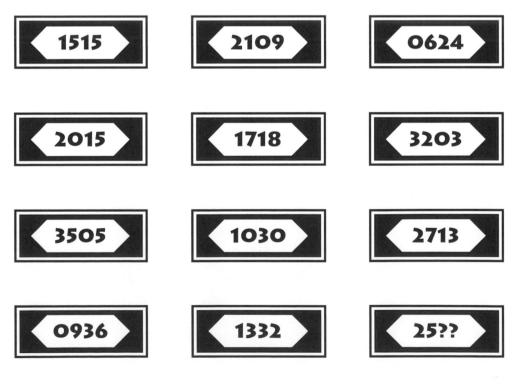

BOXING CLEVER

39

Can you work out what numbers are missing from the box on the bottom right?
(Clue: Look at each row.)

1515	2109	0624
2015	1718	3203
3505	1030	2713
0936	1332	25??

FOUR SQUARE

Fill in the empty shape and complete the puzzle.
(Clue: Look carefully at the grid to find the pattern.)

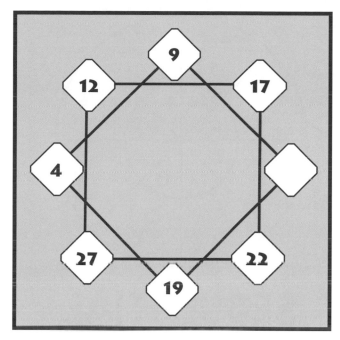

OUT OF PLACE

Which number doesn't go with the rest?

93 81 18 36 54

ET CETERA

What number must be added to continue this sequence?

5 2 8 9 11 16 14 ?

NUMBER WHEEL

Replace the question mark in this wheel with the correct number.
(Clue: Pair up each outer number with an inner number.)

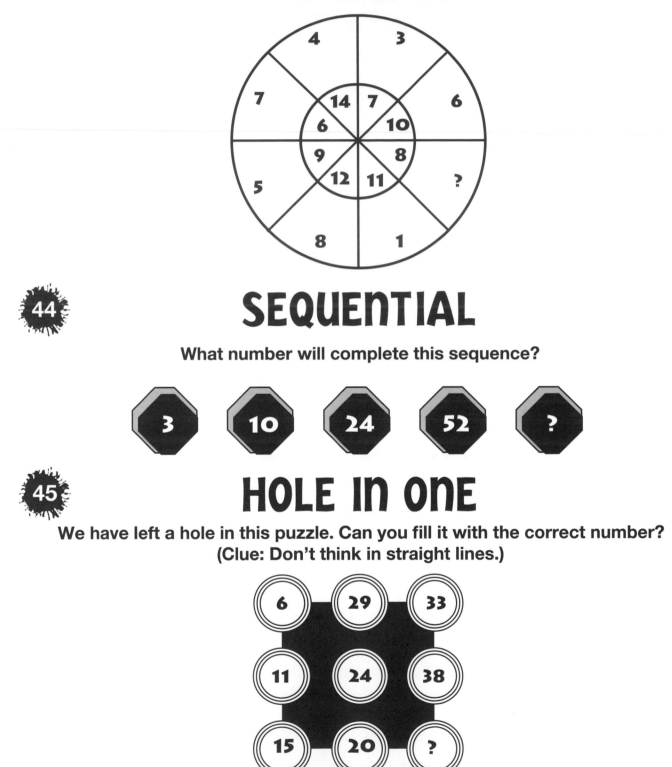

SEQUENTIAL

What number will complete this sequence?

3   10   24   52   ?

HOLE IN ONE

We have left a hole in this puzzle. Can you fill it with the correct number?
(Clue: Don't think in straight lines.)

6   29   33
11   24   38
15   20   ?

MAGIC SQUARE

By using every number between 1 and 25 can you complete this number square so that every line, up and down, left to right, and diagonal adds up to 65?

25				21
22				
			17	
5			20	1

MISFITS

One number in each square is a misfit, in other words it doesn't follow the same rules or requirements as all the others. Can you work out which one it is?

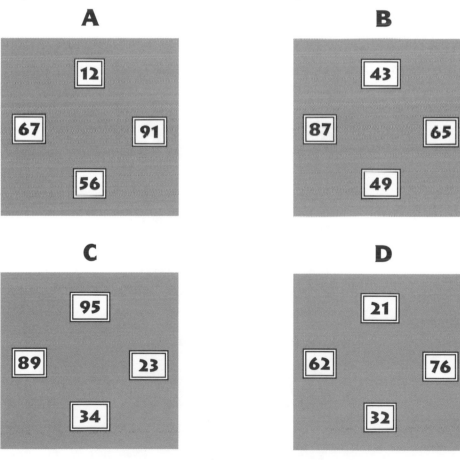

A
12
67   91
56

B
43
87   65
49

C
95
89   23
34

D
21
62   76
32

FULL HOUSE!

Using the first two houses as an example, can you work out
what number is missing from the third house?

OPTIONAL EXTRAS

Which of the three optional extra numbers at the bottom will replace the
question mark? (Clue: Don't just look from left to right.)

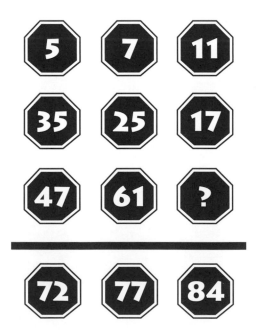

NUMBER SQUARE

50

This puzzle is a little bit different in that we have given you all the numbers already to show you what the finished teaser looks like. Can you work out why these numbers are correct?
(Clue: The center square is the key.)

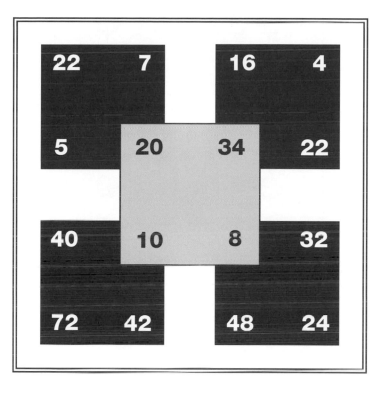

MIND BENDER

51

Every year on his birthday, Toby gets $1 from his aunt Edwina for every year of his age, that is $1 on his first birthday, $2 on his second and so on and so on. Just after his last birthday, Toby counted up how much money he had received since his first birthday, and realised it was $276 in total. How old is Toby?

52

SQUARE DEAL

Work out what number is missing and complete the puzzle.

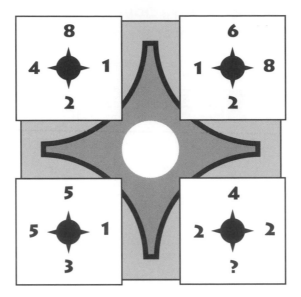

53

GONE MISSING!

The number in the middle column has gone missing, can you replace it?
(Clue: Look at both sides of the grid.)

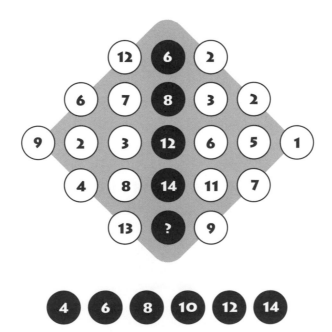

NETWORK

54

Using the first grid as an example, can you complete grids A and B?

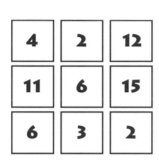

4	2	12
11	6	15
6	3	2

A

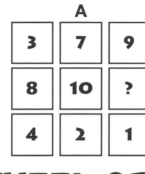

3	7	9
8	10	?
4	2	1

B

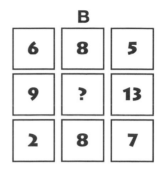

6	8	5
9	?	13
2	8	7

WHEEL SPIN

55

What numbers are missing from the last wheel?
(Clue: The wheel in the middle of the top row is the link!)

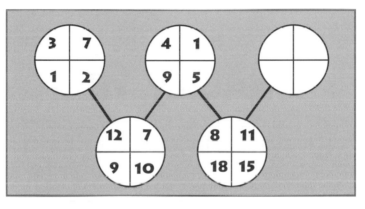

SPACE ODDITY

56

Look at our alien face very carefully and work out which number is the odd one out in each oval?

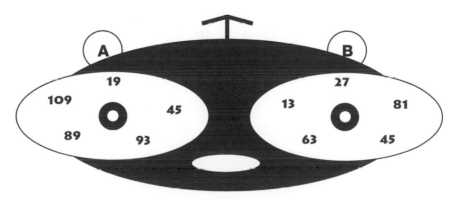

57

RING THE CHANGES

What number goes in the empty ring?

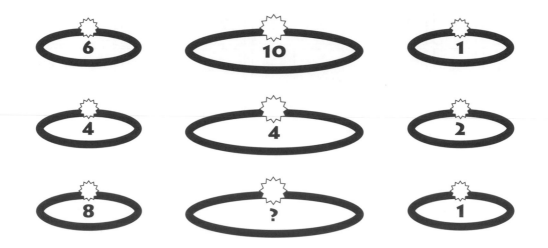

 58

WHACKY WEB

What number do you need to add in order to complete the web?
(Clue: Look at the relationship between each set of numbers.)

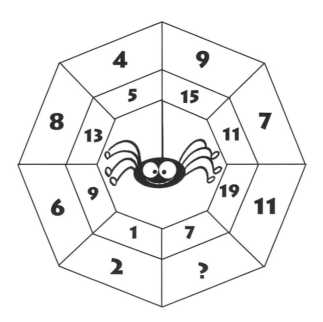

ODD ONE OUT

1

Which number is the odd one out in each oval?

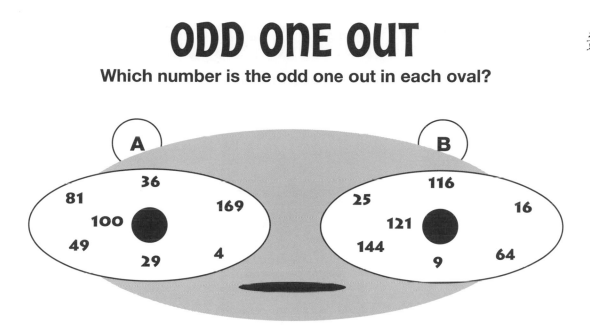

WATCH OUT

Look carefully at the sequence of watches and fill in the blank.

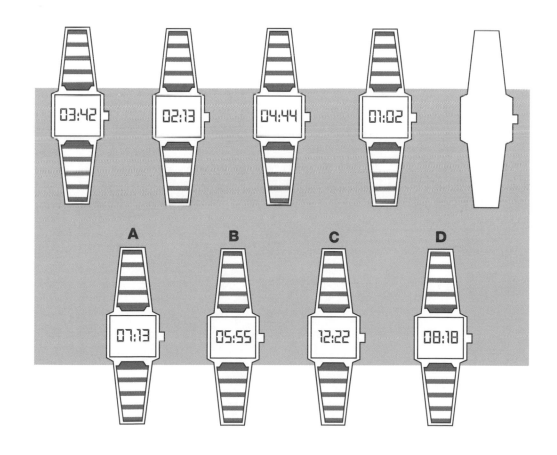

PYRAMID POSER

Work out what number goes at the top of the third pyramid.

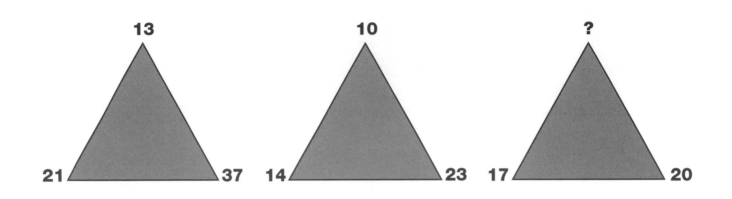

ALL SQUARE

Here is a complete puzzle—work out why it contains these numbers.
(Clue: The center square holds the answer.)

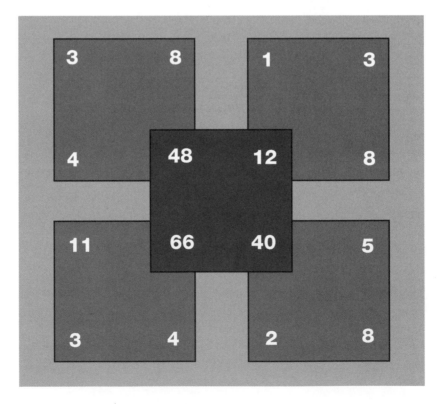

DOTTY DOMINOES

By counting the dots on these dominoes, can you work out which of the six spare pieces completes the sequence?

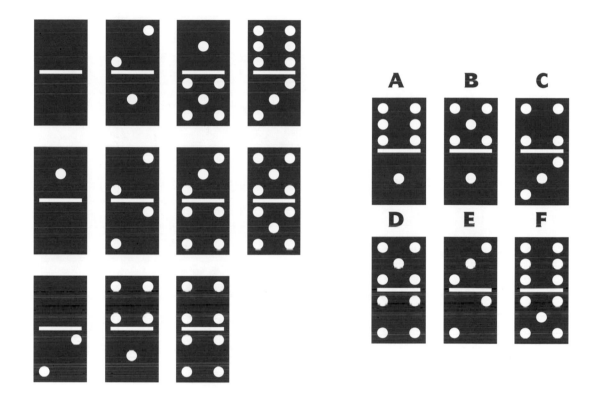

CROSS OVER

What number is missing from each puzzle?

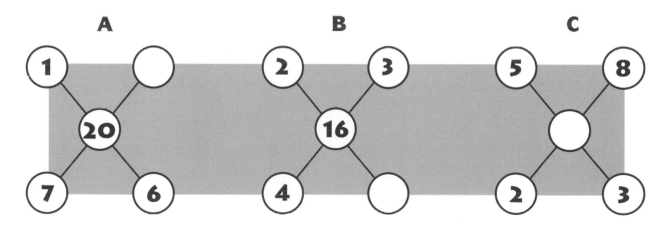

TRI–PIE

What number is missing from the empty segment?
(Clue: Look at the matching segments on each circle.)

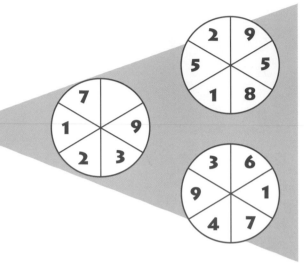

NUMBER BOX

Complete this number box by adding the correct number.
(Clue: The puzzle works up and down as well as side to side!)

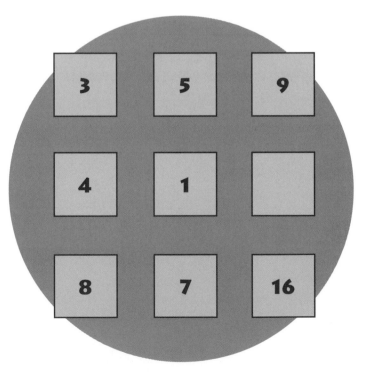

WEB WORLD

What number replaces the question mark and completes the web?

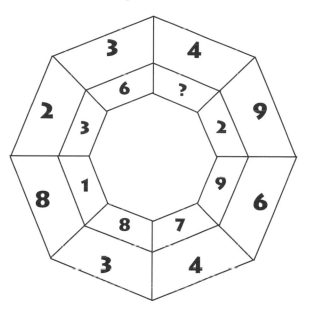

MAGIC SQUARE

Fill in the empty circle and complete the puzzle.
(Clue: Look carefully at the grid to find the pattern.)

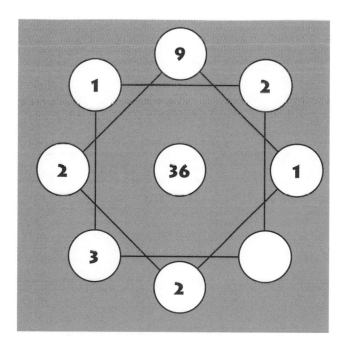

ALL STAR

By using the first two stars as a guide, can you complete this puzzle?

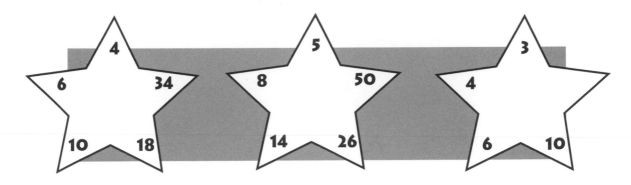

Star 1: 4, 6, 34, 10, 18

Star 2: 5, 8, 50, 14, 26

Star 3: 3, 4, 6, 10

CIRCLES

What number is needed to finish the puzzle?

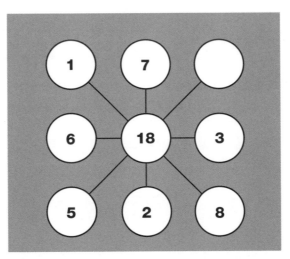

1 7

6 18 3

5 2 8

BOXING CLEVER

What number completes this sequence?

4   9   16   25   ?

MISSING NUMBERS

What numbers are missing from the empty grid?
(Clue: Look at the matching segments—the middle circle is the link!)

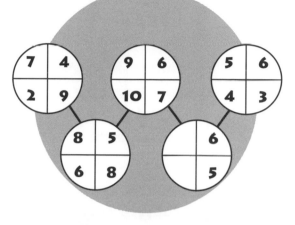

HONEYCOMB

Which number is the odd one out?

HOLE NUMBERS

Complete this puzzle by adding the correct number to the empty circle.
(Clue: Straight thinking will not help you with this one!)

FIGURE–IT–OUT

What four-figure answer is missing from the empty box?

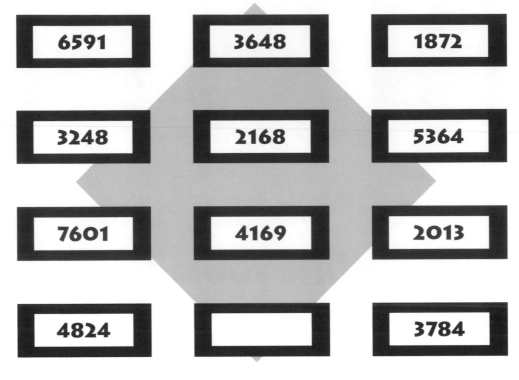

6591	3648	1872
3248	2168	5364
7601	4169	2013
4824		3784

SHAPE UP

Find the missing number to complete the puzzle.

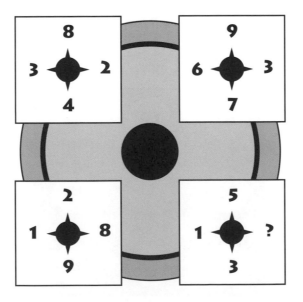

TAKE AWAY

19

What number goes in the middle oval?
(Clue: It has got nothing to do with sums!)

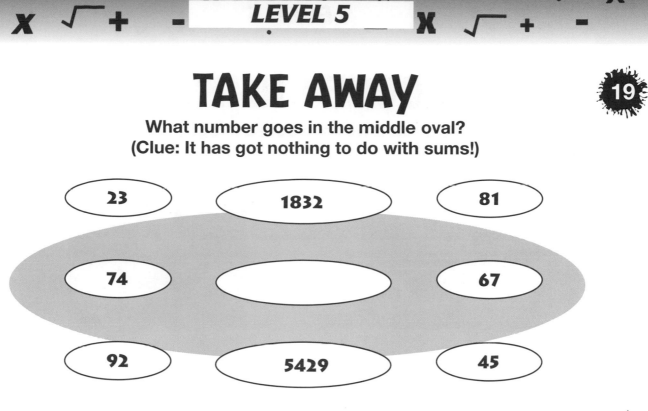

23	1832	81
74		67
92	5429	45

DOTTY!

20

Which of the bottom numbers will go into the center dot?

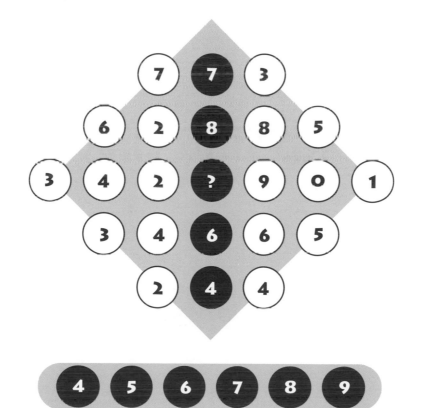

ROGUE NUMBER

In each square we have added a rogue number.
Can you work out which one it is?

A

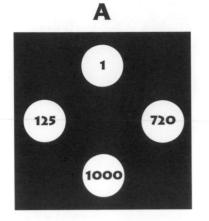

1
125   720
1000

B

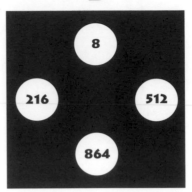

8
216   512
864

C

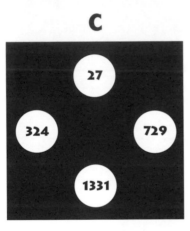

27
324   729
1331

D

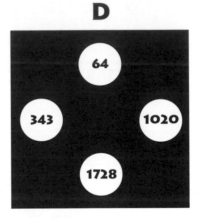

64
343   1020
1728

MISSING LINK

What number completes this chain?

2   10   3   15   8   40   33   ?

LINE UP

23

Using the same rule for every row, can you fill in the empty octagons?

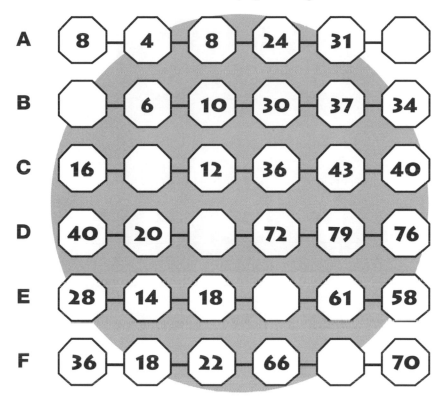

A (8)—(4)—(8)—(24)—(31)—(   )

B (   )—(6)—(10)—(30)—(37)—(34)

C (16)—(   )—(12)—(36)—(43)—(40)

D (40)—(20)—(   )—(72)—(79)—(76)

E (28)—(14)—(18)—(   )—(61)—(58)

F (36)—(18)—(22)—(66)—(   )—(70)

CHANGE IT

24

Replace the question mark with the correct number.
(Clue: Look at the relationship between the numbers in each segment.)

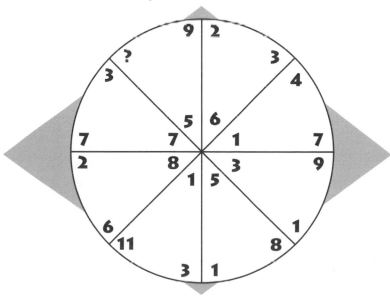

OPTIONS

Which of the three numbers at the bottom will complete this puzzle?
(Clue: Try looking up and down.)

7   18   19

14   38

10   11   34

22   24   26

NUMBER SQUARE

By using every number between 1 and 25 can you complete this number square
so that every line, up and down, left to right, and diagonal adds up to 65?

9				15
			14	
	19			
		6		24
11				

STAR STRUCK

Using the first two stars as an example, find the missing number.

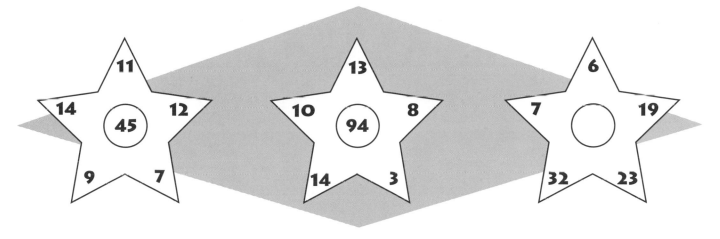

- Star 1: 11, 14, 12, 45, 9, 7
- Star 2: 13, 10, 8, 94, 14, 3
- Star 3: 6, 7, 19, 32, 23

TRIO

Using the first two circles as an example, fill in the empty segment.

- Circle 1: 2, 6, 36
- Circle 2: 4, 7, 84
- Circle 3: 5, 1

GRID LOCK

Can you work out what numbers are required to complete grids A and B?

38	28	12
57	43	91
32	71	31

24	27	51
43	54	61
31		31

A

17	28	81
59	43	12
22		21

B

LINES OF THOUGHT

Put on your thinking caps and work out what number is missing from each line of octagons, use the first line as an example.

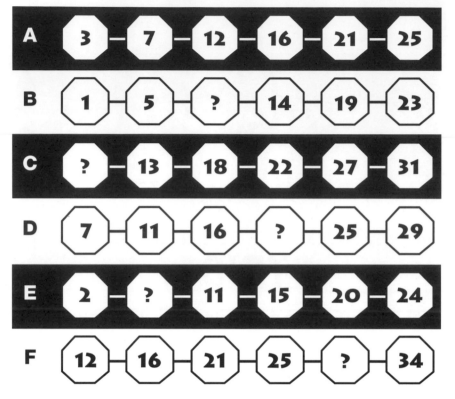

A 3 — 7 — 12 — 16 — 21 — 25

B 1 — 5 — ? — 14 — 19 — 23

C ? — 13 — 18 — 22 — 27 — 31

D 7 — 11 — 16 — ? — 25 — 29

E 2 — ? — 11 — 15 — 20 — 24

F 12 — 16 — 21 — 25 — ? — 34

PYRAMID POINTERS

What number goes on the top point of pyramid C?

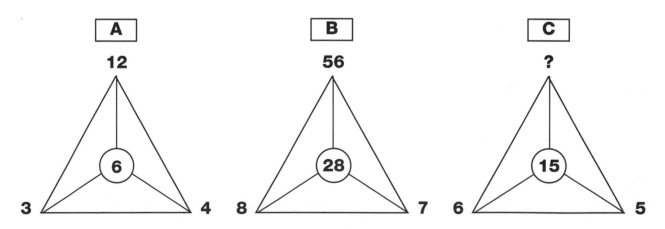

A

12

6

3   4

B

56

28

8   7

C

?

15

6   5

TIME OUT

What time should be shown on the blank watch at the end of the top line?

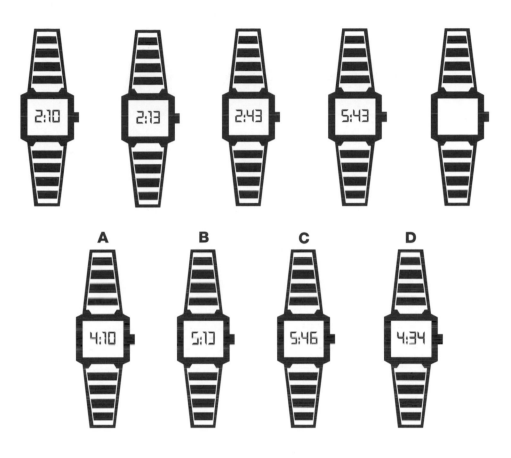

2:10   2:13   2:43   5:43   [blank]

A 4:10   **B** 5:17   **C** 5:46   **D** 4:34

STAR STRUCK

Can you complete this puzzle by using the first two stars as a guide?

Star 1: 2, 5, 8, 2, 0
Star 2: 5, 9, 2, 1, 7
Star 3: ?, 7, 5, 2, 4

FIGURE IT OUT

Complete this puzzle by adding the correct number.
(Clue: Try looking at the puzzle from all directions.)

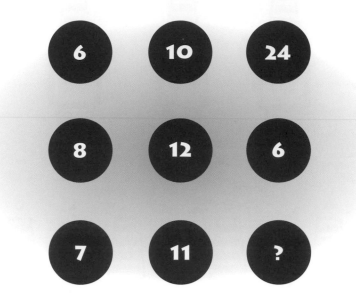

SLICED UP!

Can you work out what number is missing from the empty segment?
(Clue: Try stepping from one circle to another.)

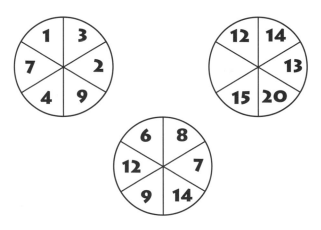

DOTTY DOMINOES!

Which of the six spare dominoes completes this dotty sequence?

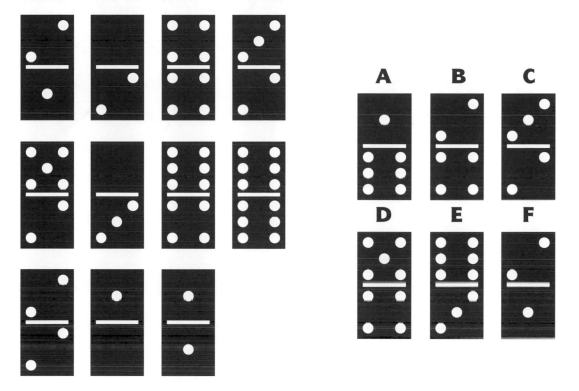

CIRCLES

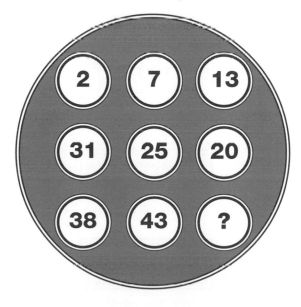

Fill in the missing number.

2	7	13
31	25	20
38	43	?

DIGITAL DISCS

Using the first two discs as an example, fill in the empty segment.

BOXING CLEVER

Can you work out what number is missing from the empty box?
(Clue: Look at the separate boxes in each row.)

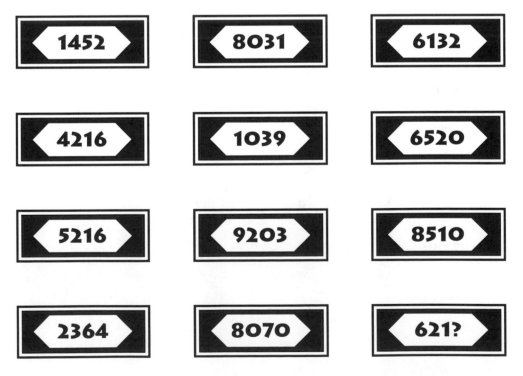

1452	8031	6132
4216	1039	6520
5216	9203	8510
2364	8070	621?

FOUR SQUARE

Fill in the empty shape and complete the puzzle.
(Clue: Look carefully at the grid to find the pattern.)

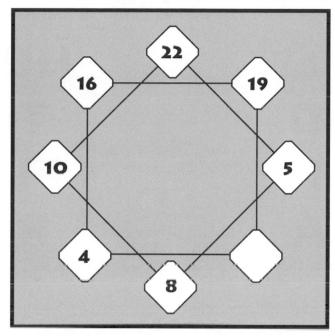

OUT OF PLACE

Which number doesn't go with the rest?

ET CETERA

What number must be added to continue this sequence?

ADD-A-LETTER

Add the same letter to all these words to make a brand new one.
e.g. The letter 't' can be added to moral to make mortal.

S^tILL   ^tHORN

S^tAND   TOO^t

^tRIM   FLUE^t

PLEA^t   ^tRUE

HIDDEN WORDS

The name of a gemstone has been hidden in each of these sentences.
Can you use your powers of observation and find them all?
e.g. a man's name has been hidden in this sentence: "We hadn't given
up hope terriers would be banned from the dog show next week."

1. Rub your eyes if you don't believe it

2. Over Christmas the wages are good. I am on double time.

3. When you stop, always check in your mirror.

4. From the cliff top, azure waters could be seen for miles.

5. I can make a rabbit appear like magic.

ODD ONE OUT

3

Which of these capital cities is the odd one out and why?

ROME

MELBOURNE

PARIS

X LONGON _No R_

MADRID

FIRST & LAST

4

Which letter can replace the last letter of each word in the first column
and the first letter of each word in the second column?
Write your answer in the box in the middle and make a new word going down.

TALL	K	PILL
SEVER	n	FEW
MIND	i	ACE
SCARE	f	DUEL
TILT	e	AGO

Clue: Cutting tool

CROSSWORD

A regular crossword for you to enjoy. Try working it out by using the clues, but if you get stuck, the answers appear on the bottom of the page in alphabetical order.

ACROSS

1 - Animal with scales and fins (4)
5 - Very hard wood (4)
8 - Gradually wear away (5)
10 - A continent (6)
11 - Thin, pointed piece of ice hanging down (6)
12 - Soil in which plants grow (5)
14 - Container for pencils (4)
16 - Kiln for drying hops (4)
19 - Sloping platform (4)
20 - Diesel oil (4)
21 - Germany's neighbor (7)
22 - Better than any other (4)
24 - Kiss quickly (4)
26 - Line of coral just below the ocean's surface (4)
28 - Swelling on the eyelid (4)
30 - A play in which most of the words are sung (5)
34 - Stop working due to old age (6)
35 - Deer's horn (6)
36 - Minister's house (5)
37 - Bigger amount (4)
38 - Knob on the sole of a soccer boot (4)

DOWN

1 - Give food to a person (4)
2 - A small river (6)
3 - Size of a flat surface (4)
4 - Get a book ready for printing (4)
6 - Words that explain why you have done something wrong (6)
7 - Was aware of (4)
8 - Sharp-pointed sword
9 - Sound that bounces off something solid (4)
13 - Style of jazz music (7)
14 - Pole tossed at Scottish Highland Games (5)
15 - Sudden outbreak (5)
17 - Change the use of something (5)
18 - Ceasefire (5)
23 - Slender game dog (6)
25 - Hole for threading laces through (6)
27 - Document with spaces to write in (4)
28 - Sensible (4)
29 - Percussion instrument (4)
31 - Fuel cut from bogs (4)
32 - Coarse file (4)
33 - Barney Rubble's friend, - - - - Flintstone (4)

ADAPT
ANTLER
AREA
AUSTRIA
BEST
CABER
CASE
DERV
DRUM
EARTH
ECHO
EDIT
EPEE
ERODE

EUROPE
EXCUSE
EYELET
FEED
FISH
FORM
FRED
ICICLE
KNEW
MANSE
MORE
OAST
OPERA
PEAT

PECK
RAGTIME
RAMP
RASP
REEF
RETIRE
SANE
SETTER
SPATE
STREAM
STUD
STYE
TEAK
TRUCE

WHEEL SPIN

Which letter replaces the question mark and completes the word?

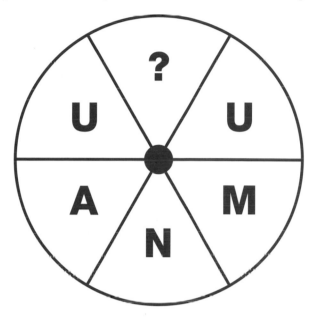

NEXT-IN-LINE

Which of the words below will logically follow on from these?

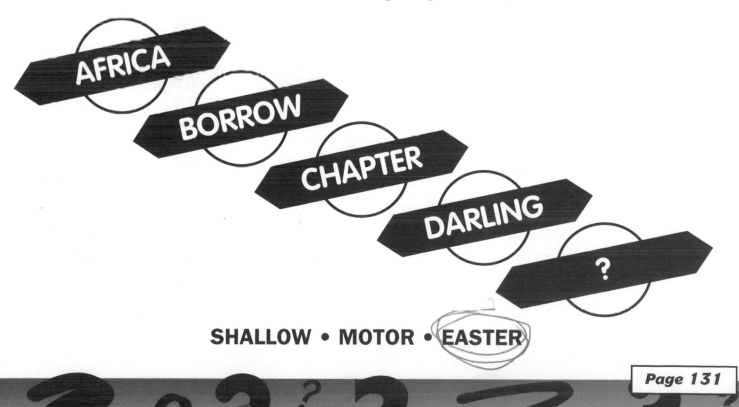

AFRICA

BORROW

CHAPTER

DARLING

?

SHALLOW • MOTOR • EASTER

8 LINK WORDS

Make a new word or phrase by placing the same five-letter word in front or behind each of these words. e.g. black in front of bird will make blackbird.

light

- - - - - **HOUSE**   **HEAD** - - -- -

- - - - - **BULB**   - - - - - **BRIGADE**

SUN - - - - -   **DAY** - - - - -

9 X—WORDS

Fill in the empty circles and complete the puzzle.
(Clue: Don't look at the shape of the grid—the shape is in the answer)

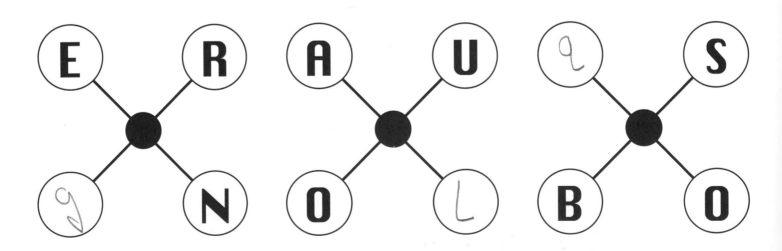

CODEBREAKER

10

Every letter of the alphabet has been replaced with a number. Your job is to work out which number represents each letter and write it in the grid. We have entered the word EARL so you know that 4 = L, 11 = E, 12 = A and 21 = R.
If you get stuck there are two extra letters at the bottom of the page.

1	2	3	4	5	6	7	8	9	10	11	12	13
Z	P	B	L	H	S	M	Y	Q	X	E	A	N

14	15	16	17	18	19	20	21	22	23	24	25	26
F	K	V	G	I	W	D	R	U	O	J	T	C

6 = S 25 = T

SCRAMBLED!

The answers to these clues have all been scrambled up.
Can you work out what each answer is?

1 **DENICTCA** Mishap

2 **OTHPFOTA** Sidewalk

3 **SEHRDWIHSA** Kitchen appliance

4 **PSAGZLIJUEZW** Cut-up picture game (6, 6)

5 **NWBOREI** Junior Girl Scout

6 **MNTOIEPMA** Theatrical entertainment

7 **RHEATEC** Tutor

8 **MASOPHO** Hair cleaner

9 **LIHJEYLFS** Sea creature

10 **VPRIMEO** Make better

11 **SIWHRPE** Talk in hushed tones

12 **OTERNFANO** Part of the day

FIVE STAR

We have taken a letter away from each star and replaced it with a question mark.
Can you work out which letter is needed to complete the word in each shape?
(Clue: Look for things you might find in the garden)

1

Y
S   P
N   ?

2

A
?   I
Y   S

3

P
?   Y
O   P

ROGUE WORD

Work out which one of these words does
not belong in this group.

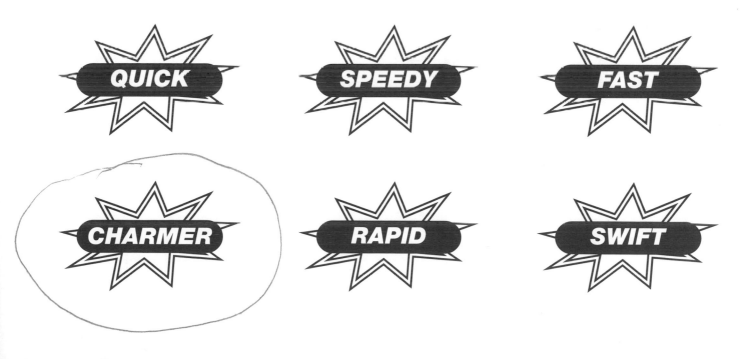

QUICK

SPEEDY

FAST

CHARMER

RAPID

SWIFT

14 JIG-SAW JUMBLE

Put these blocks of letters back into the grid in the correct order. When complete the grid will show words reading both across and down, separated by a bold line. We have replaced one block and put in the bold lines to help you.

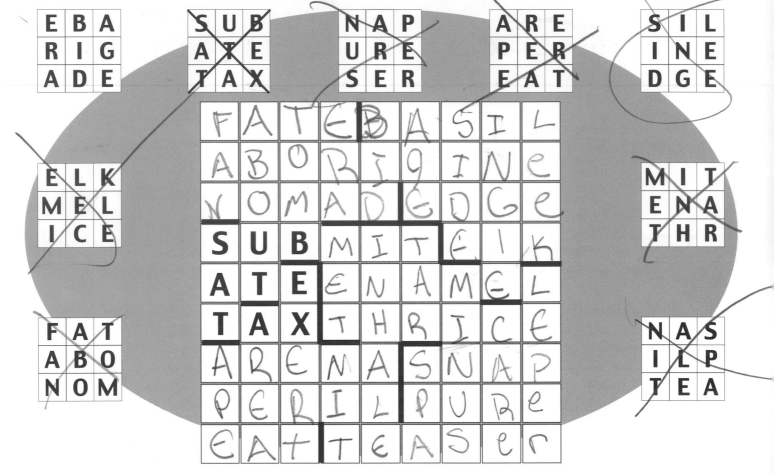

15 SCRAMBLE

Can you rearrange these letters and make another eight-letter word?

CREATION

REACTION

Clue: Response

TWINS

Pair up each word in the first circle with a word of similar meaning in the second. When you have finished, one word from each circle will be left without a twin.

1

DAMP

NEVER

ANGRY

TALLEST

SMART

LARGE

PLEASED

2

HIGHEST

CROSS

HAPPY

BIG

MOIST

TOTAL

CLEVER

ALL CHANGE

Rearrange the words in each row to make a new one. Write it in the same line in the second box. Sometimes you will be able to make more than one word, so we have given a clue to help you. Another five-letter word will appear in the shaded column.

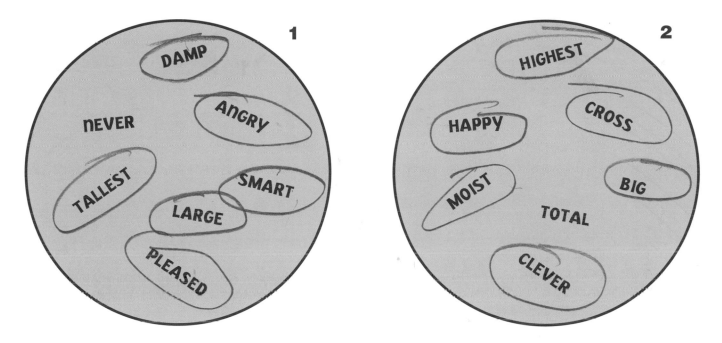

S	N	A	K	E
B	R	E	A	D
G	L	A	R	E
S	T	A	L	K
P	E	A	C	H

S	N	E	A	K
B	e	a	r	d
r	e	a	g	l
T	A	I	K	S
c	h	e	a	p

1 - Cheat

2 - Facial hair

3 - Queenly

4 - Chats

5 - Not expensive

Clue: Large bird of prey

18

VOWEL PLAY

All the vowels have been taken out of this crossword and placed in boxes next to the grid. Can you replace them all in their correct positions?

19

ANAGRAM TIMER

The answer to each of the clues is an anagram of the word above and below it, plus or minus one letter.

1 - To sweet talk

2 - Injure, damage

3 - Upper limb

4 - Female horse

5 - Vision seen in sleep

INCOMPLETE

20

One of every letter of the alphabet has been taken from this puzzle.
Can you put them all back into their correct positions?

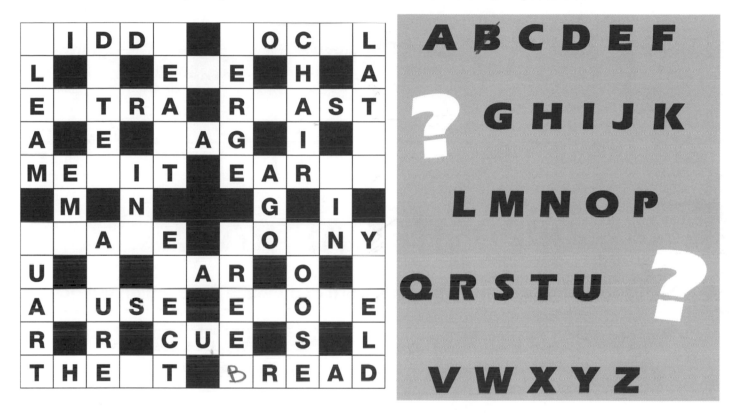

STEP LADDER

21

By changing one letter each step, can you turn LOVE to HATE in three moves?

LOVE

Dove — Bird of peace

Dote — Be fond of

Date — Romantic appointment

HATE

PROVERBS

Here are three very famous proverbs with some missing words.
From the choices we have given you can you complete them all?

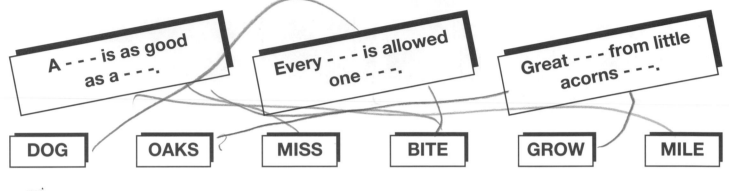

A - - - is as good as a - - -.

Every - - - is allowed one - - -.

Great - - - from little acorns - - -.

| DOG | OAKS | MISS | BITE | GROW | MILE |

OPPOSITES ATTRACT

Match the four words on the left with a word of opposite meaning on the right.

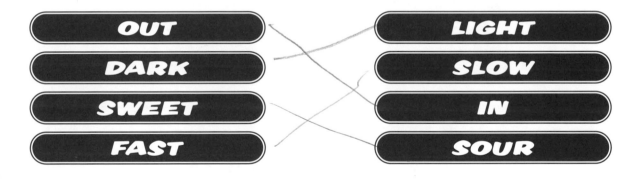

OUT	LIGHT
DARK	SLOW
SWEET	IN
FAST	SOUR

MIX-UP

Unravel the letters to find four vegetables.

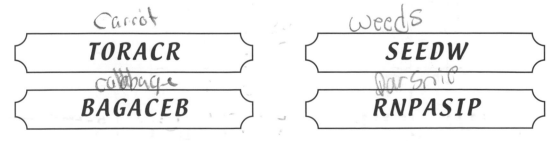

Carrot

TORACR

weeds

SEEDW

cabbage

BAGACEB

parsnip

RNPASIP

PICTURE THIS

25

Look at each picture carefully and write the initial letter in the corresponding box underneath. When you have finished an eight-letter word will be spelt out.

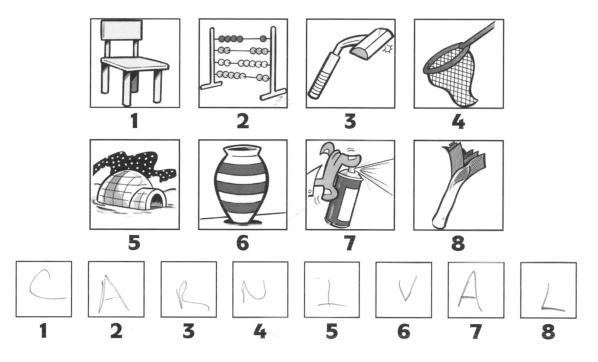

C	A	R	N	I	V	A	L
1	2	3	4	5	6	7	8

QUICK CHANGE

26

Rearrange the words on each line to make a new word using the clues to help you. Write this new word in the right-hand box and you will discover a new word appearing in the shaded column.

S	E	R	V	E
W	H	E	A	L
P	L	E	A	D
W	I	N	G	S
T	U	T	O	R

verse — 1 - Part of a poem

whale — 2 - Large sea mammal

pedal — 3 - Foot lever on a bicycle

swing — 4 - Garden toy

trout — 5 - Freshwater fish

Clue to hidden word: Something you listen to.

CROSSWORD

A regular crossword puzzle for you to solve. Try working it out by using the clues first, but if you get stuck we have listed all the words you need to finish the puzzle in alphabetical order at the bottom of the page.

ACROSS

3 – Avid, passionate (9)
8 – Shine (4)
9 – Apple – – –, tasty snack (8)
10 – Come to an end (6)
13 – Frenzied (5)
14 – Disease also known as lockjaw (7)
15 – Edible fish (3)
16 – Convent (7)
17 – Big (5)
21 – Leave empty (6)
22 – Produce (8)
23 – Paws (4)
24 – Figurine (9)

DOWN

1 – Contract (9)
2 – Constituent part (9)
4 – Daisy–like flower (5)
5 – Reached (7)
6 – False god (4)
7 – Incite by encouragement (4)
11 – Built up (9)
12 – Female movie–theater attendant (9)
14 – Object to play with (3)
15 – Burn to ashes (7)
18 – Ward off (5)
19 – Dissolve, thaw (4)
20 – Opening for fumes to escape through (4)

ABET • AGREEMENT • ARRIVED • ASTER • AVERT • COD • COMPONENT • CREMATE • EXPIRE
FANATICAL • FEET • GENERATE • GLOW • IDOL • INCREASED • LARGE • MANIC • MELT
NUNNERY • STATUETTE • TETANUS • TOY • TURNOVER • USHERETTE • VACATE • VENT

TRIANGLE TWINS

28

Pair up each word in the first triangle with a word of similar meaning in the second.
When you have finished, one word from each triangle will be left without a twin.

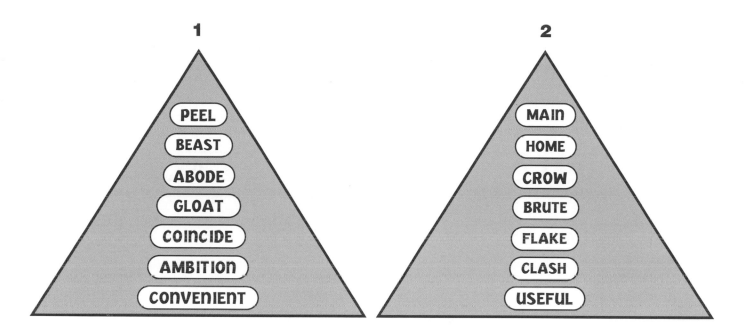

1

PEEL
BEAST
ABODE
GLOAT
COINCIDE
AMBITION
CONVENIENT

2

MAIN
HOME
CROW
BRUTE
FLAKE
CLASH
USEFUL

STAR STRUCK

29

A letter has been removed from each star and replaced with a question mark.
Which letter is needed to complete the word in each shape?
(Clue: Egg-layers.)

1

W
S   I
T   ?

2

I
?   N
O   R

3

E
?   N
A   R

30

ODDITY

Can you work out which of these words is the odd one out and why?

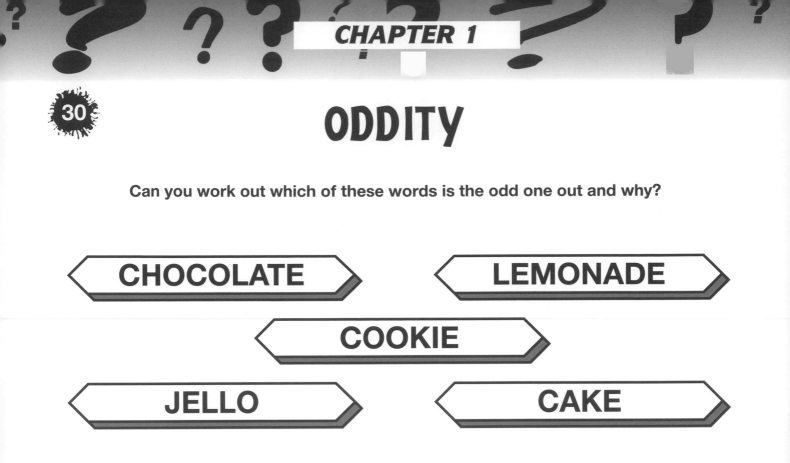

CHOCOLATE

LEMONADE

COOKIE

JELLO

CAKE

31

DARTBOARD

Fill the shaded segments with one of the five letters below to make four different four-letter words, each reading out from the center.

A A D R T

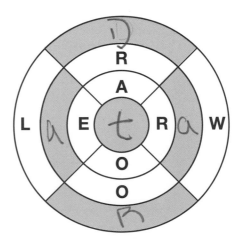

FIRST & LAST

Replace the last letter of each word in column 1, and the first letter of
each word in column 2 with the same letter of the alphabet. Put this letter
in the middle box to make a new word reading down.

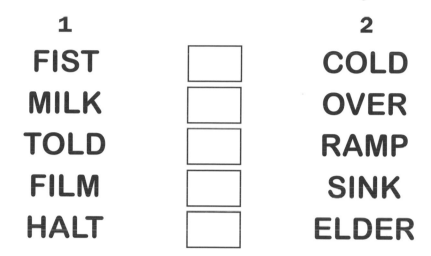

1		2
FIST		COLD
MILK		OVER
TOLD		RAMP
FILM		SINK
HALT		ELDER

Clue: It might be the first word you say!

LINK UP

Make a new word or phrase by placing the same three-letter word in front or behind
each of these words. e.g. Show in front of boat will make showboat.

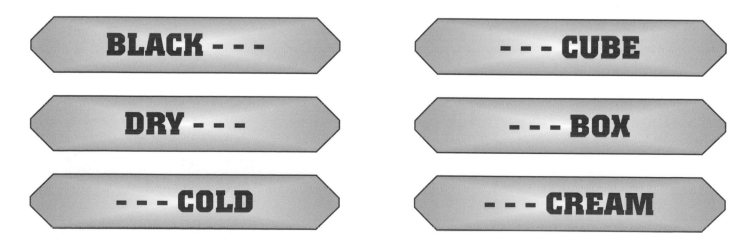

BLACK - - -

- - - CUBE

DRY - - -

- - - BOX

- - - COLD

- - - CREAM

34

ALL MIXED UP

The answers to these clues are given on the right-hand side but the letters have been all mixed up. Can you unscramble them all and solve the puzzles?

1 - Accident victim

2 - Looked at closely

3 - Sweet-smelling   Fragrance

4 - Football official   linesman

5 - Women's underwear

6 - Wedding ceremony

7 - Street footpath

8 - Steady improvement

9 - Intentional damage

10 - Burn slowly

11 - Unexpected occurrence

12 - Move from one place to another

LTUACASY

MIXDEANE

TRAGAFRN

SLIANEMN

EGIRLNEI

AIREGARM

WSAIELKD

SORRPGES

GABOTESA

DRUMLOSE

SEURPISR

FERSTANR

ABACUS

Slide the abacus beads across the wires to form four colors reading downwards. All the beads will be used. Keep in mind that the beads are on wires and cannot jump over one another. An empty abacus is provided for you to work in.

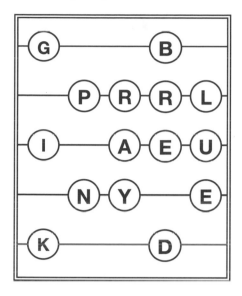

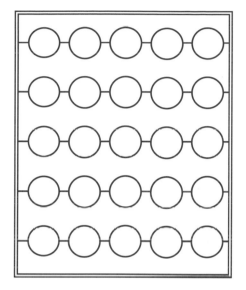

WHAT COMES NEXT?

Which of the words below will logically follow on from these?

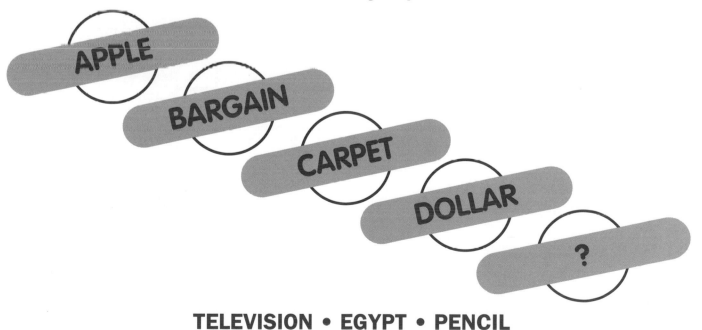

TELEVISION • EGYPT • PENCIL

37

ANAGRAMS

Unscramble the letters in this word to make another one.

A	U	C	T	I	O	N

Clue: Formal warning.

38

BITS 'n' PIECES

Put these blocks of letters back into the grid in the correct order. When complete the grid will show words reading both across and down, separated by a bold line. We have replaced one block and put in the bold lines to help you.

I	R	S
D	O	H
L	U	E

A	L	L
S	E	A
H	A	R

R	A	G
C	R	E
E	N	T

A	D	O
R	E	S
T	R	E

C	H	A
A	I	R
R	M	C

A	R	R
T	E	A
A	S	S

E	G	O
R	E	P
A	L	A

E	S	T
F	E	E
O	W	N

R	E	C
I	N	A
A	T	L

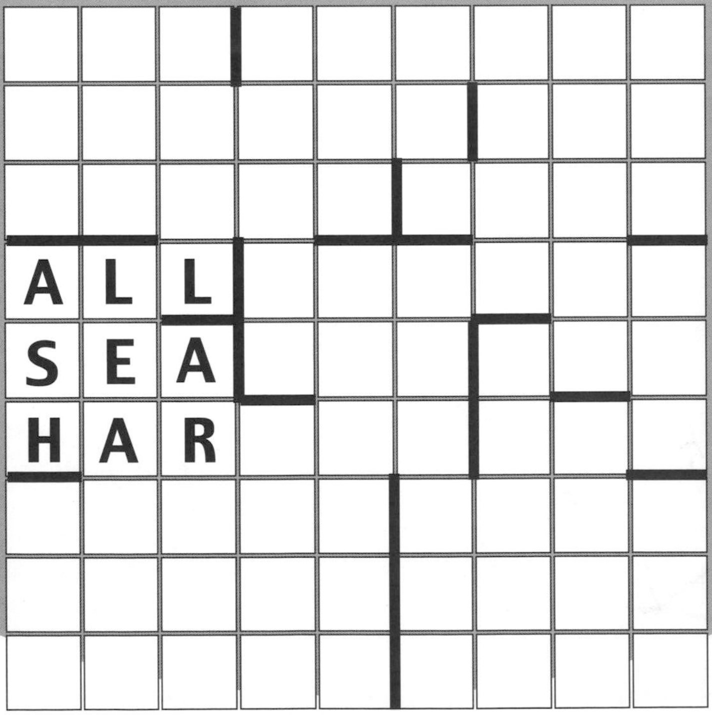

TIME FOR AN ANAGRAM

The answer to each of the clues is an anagram of the word above and below it, plus or minus one letter.

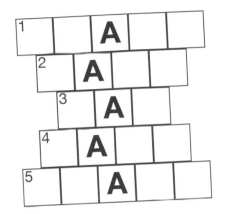

1 - Speedway circuit

2 - Small nail

3 - Feline animal

4 - Not fiction

5 - Art

WHAT, nO VOWELS!

We have taken all the vowels out of this crossword and placed them to the right of the grid. Can you replace them all in their correct positions and complete the puzzle?

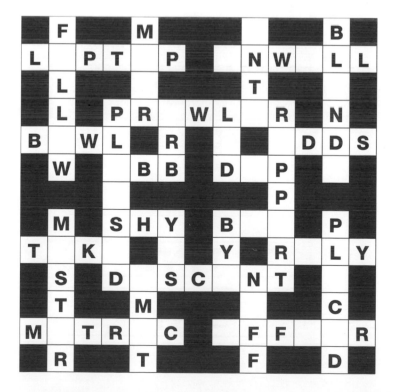

A A A A A A A A A

E E E E E E E E E E E

I I I

O O O O O O O

U

41

HIDDEN WORDS

The name of a dog can be found in each of these sentences.
Using your powers of observation, see if you can find them all.
e.g. in the following sentence we have hidden the word 'corgi':
Although Mike had changed the de<u>cor, Gi</u>llian still wanted to move house.

1 - When I listened to my album by Blur, Cheryl went out.

2 - The competition was won by Jack. Albert finished last.

3 - The man was caught trying to rob eagle's nests last week.

4 - When I saw the bridge's span, I elected to go by boat.

5 - A maniac Ollie certainly was, but we all liked him.

42

ADD-A-LETTER

Add the letter 'A' to all these words to make a brand new one.
You can put it at the beginning of the word, at the end, or even in the middle.

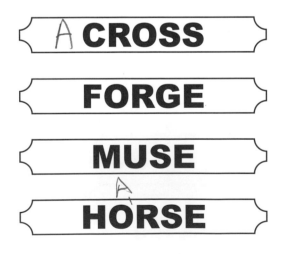

A **CROSS**

FORGE

MUSE

HORSE

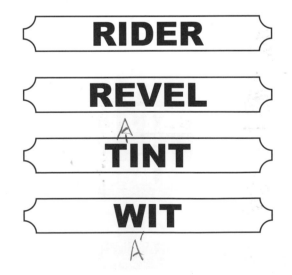

RIDER

REVEL

TINT

WIT

CODEBREAKER

43

Every letter of the alphabet has been replaced with a number. Your job is to work out
which number represents each letter and write it in the grid. We have entered the
word EARN so you know that 21 = E, 5 = A, 26 = R, and 2 = N.
If you get stuck there are two extra letters at the bottom of the page.

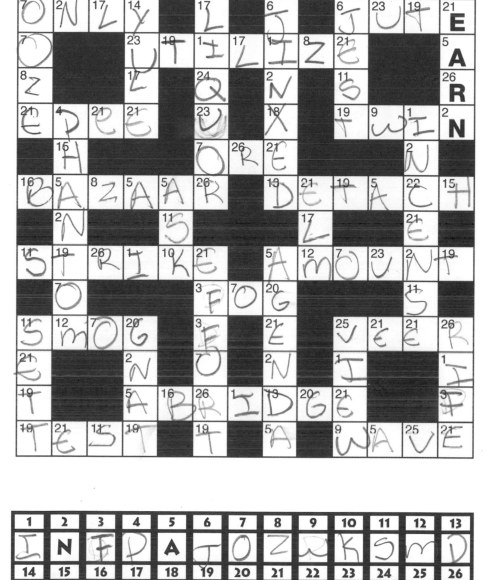

1	2	3	4	5	6	7	8	9	10	11	12	13
I	N	F	P	A	O	Z	K	S	M	D		
14	**15**	**16**	**17**	**18**	**19**	**20**	**21**	**22**	**23**	**24**	**25**	**26**
Y	H	B	L	X	T	G	E	C	U	Q	V	R

11 = S   19 = T

STEP BY STEP

By changing one letter each step, turn WEST to VALE in three moves.

WEST	*Vest*	*vast*	*vase*	VALE
	Winter underwear	Gigantic	Container for cut flowers	

OPPOSITES ATTRACT

Match the four words on the left with a word of opposite meaning on the right.

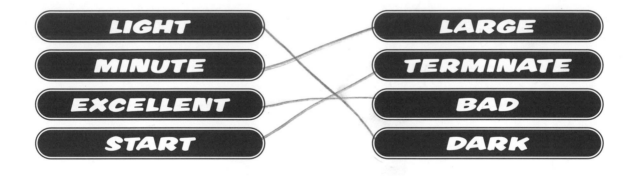

LIGHT	LARGE
MINUTE	TERMINATE
EXCELLENT	BAD
START	DARK

INSIDE OUT

We have taken a four-letter word out of each of the words listed below. Can you work out which word should go back 'inside' and make a complete word again?
e.g. OVER should go back inside the letters PR - - - - BS to make PROVERBS.

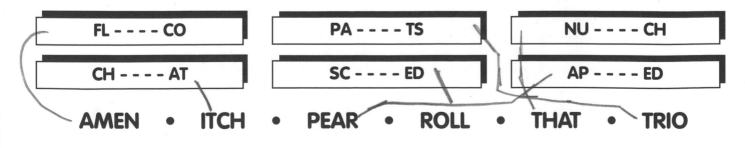

| FL - - - - CO | PA - - - - TS | NU - - - - CH |
| CH - - - - AT | SC - - - - ED | AP - - - - ED |

AMEN • ITCH • PEAR • ROLL • THAT • TRIO

MISSING LETTERS

47

One of each letter of the alphabet has been taken from this crossword grid.
Can you put them all back into their correct positions?

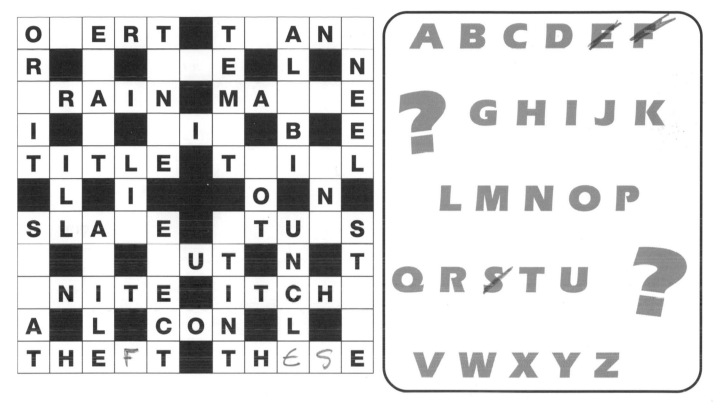

IN A STEW!

48

Find four European capital cities by rearranging the letters in each box.

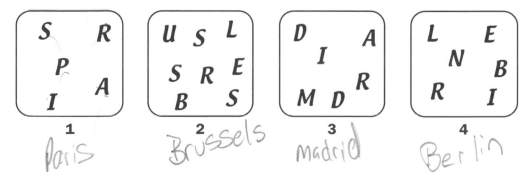

1 Paris   2 Brussels   3 Madrid   4 Berlin

ADD-A-LETTER

Add the same letter to all these words to make a brand new one.
e.g. The letter 't' can be added to moral to make mortal.

CATER	**SLAT**
PAT	**SPLIT**
ICE	**PIE**
DUE	**BET**

HIDDEN WORDS

The name of a bird has been hidden in each of these sentences.
Can you use your powers of observation and find them all?
e.g. A man's name has been hidden in this sentence: "We hadn't given
up ho<u>pe ter</u>riers would be banned from the dog show next week."

1 - Deciding to quit smoking, Joe took his final puff in March.

2 - After hearing Tom's plea, Glen let the matter drop.

3 - Sarah sat on the bench awkwardly.

4 - Andrew felt ashamed as he put back items he stole.

5 - As John scores par, rows erupt on the golf course.

ODD ONE OUT

3

Which of these colors is the odd one out and why?

BLUE

RED

GREEN

YELLOW

✗ BROWN ✗

NO E

FIRST & LAST

4

Which letter can replace the last letter of each word in the first column
and the first letter of each word in the second column?
Write your answer in the box in the middle and make a new word going down.

BASIN		BLOT
TUNE		ICE
CLAP	M	RICE
TOLL		WENT
STALE		BEAD
TALK		ILK

Clue: Wax light

CROSSWORD

A regular crossword for you to enjoy. Try working it out by using the clues, but if you get stuck, the answers appear on the bottom of the page in alphabetical order.

ACROSS

1 - Line of people one behind the other (4)
5 - Person in charge (4)
8 - Indicate (5)
10 - Clothes (6)
11 - Boil over with anger (6)
12 - Messenger sent by God (5)
14 - Actor, - - - Bean (4)
16 - Two things that belong together (4)
19 - British nobleman (4)
20 - Spot of ink spilt on something (4)
21 - Strong wind storm (7)
22 - Container for cut flowers (4)
24 - Cheerless, dingy (4)
26 - Novel's main character (4)
28 - University official (4)
30 - In which place? (5)
34 - Girl's name (6)
35 - Heart disease (6)
36 - Quick, speedy (5)
37 - Move round (4)
38 - Used to be (4)

DOWN

1 - Flat open tart (4)
2 - More recent (6)
3 - Word said at the end of a prayer (4)
4 - Otherwise (4)
6 - Popular soup flavor (6)
7 - Appear (4)
8 - Gulf country, capital Tehran (4)
9 - Short sudden cry (4)
13 - Hard rock (7)
14 - Prince Andrew's ex-wife (5)
15 - Make different (5)
17 - Place to live in (5)
18 - Ancient Italian (5)
23 - Section (6)
25 - Deep steep-sided valley (6)
27 - Michael - - - -, English soccer player (4)
28 - Declare to be false (4)
29 - Agreement, treaty (4)
31 - Soft covering that grows on the head (4)
32 - Speed of progress (4)
33 - Country road (4)

ABODE
ALTER
AMEN
ANGEL
ANGINA
ANTHEA
ATTIRE
BLOT
BOSS
DEAN
DENY
DRAB
EARL
ELSE

FILE
FLAN
GRANITE
HAIR
HERO
IMPLY
IRAN
LANE
LATTER
NIFTY
OWEN
OXTAIL
PACT
PAIR

RATE
RAVINE
ROMAN
SARAH
SEAN
SECTOR
SEEM
SEETHE
TORNADO
TURN
VASE
WERE
WHERE
YELP

WHEEL SPIN

6

Which letter replaces the question mark and completes the word?

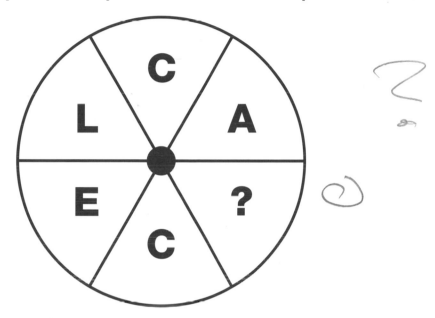

NEXT-IN-LINE

7

Which of the words below will logically follow on from these?

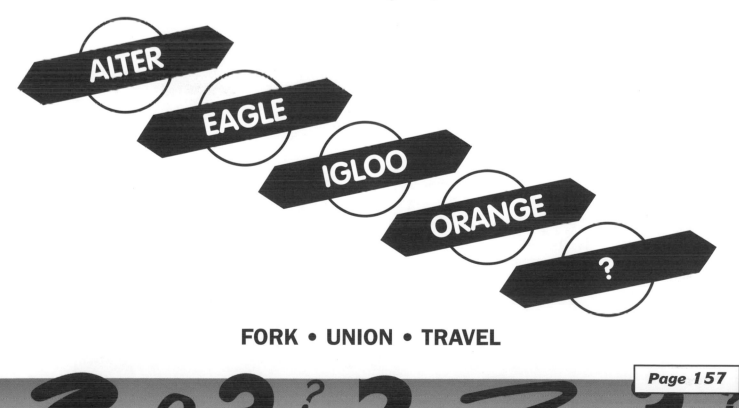

FORK • UNION • TRAVEL

LINK WORDS

Make a new word or phrase by placing the same six-letter word in front or behind each of these words. e.g. black in front of bird will make blackbird.

- - - SLIPPERS

- - - TILES

MAGIC - - -

RED - - -

- - - SWEEPER

- - - BAG

X—WORDS

Fill in the empty circles and complete the puzzle.
(Clue: Don't look at the shape of the puzzle or your number's up!)

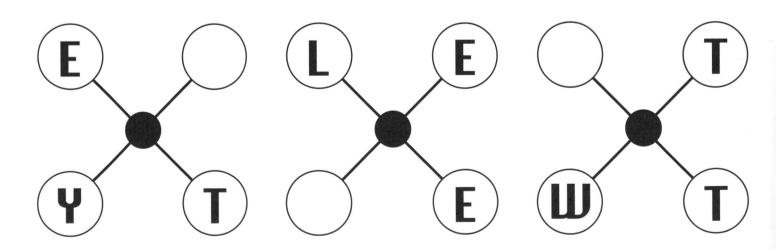

CODEBREAKER

Every letter of the alphabet has been replaced with a number. Your job is to work out which number represents each letter and write it in the grid. We have entered the word NEAT so you know that 13 = N, 9 = E, 18 = A and 6 = T.
If you get stuck there are two extra letters at the bottom of the page.

25 = R 22 = L

SCRAMBLED!

The answers to these clues have all been scrambled up.
Can you work out what each answer is?

1 **RIRGDEOP** Breakfast food

2 **OLREDHSU** Part of the body

3 **TACAPIL** Main town *Capital*

4 **RHTYISO** Study of past events *history*

5 **AFNUFRI** Amusement park *Fun Fair*

6 **GIACMAIN** Wizard *Magician*

7 **LSABELBA** Team game *Baseball*

8 **ANUPYPH** Sad *unhappy*

9 **RIOTSUT** Holidaymaker

10 **BHGERONI** Person next door *neighbor*

11 **TNEAENC** School cafe

12 **AINOTST** Police building *Station*

FIVE STAR

12

We have taken a letter away from each star and replaced it with a question mark.
Can you work out which letter is needed to complete the word in each shape?
(Clue: Look for things that fly)

1

E
L E
? A

2
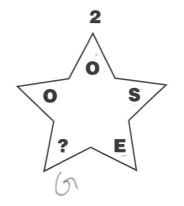
O
O S
? E
G

3

H
C F
? I

ROGUE WORD

13

Work out which one of these words does
not belong in this group.

FRIGHT

HORROR

SCARE

TERROR

ALARM

WASTE

JIG-SAW JUMBLE

Put these blocks of letters back into the grid in the correct order. When complete the grid will show words reading both across and down, separated by a bold line. We have replaced one block and put in the bold lines to help you.

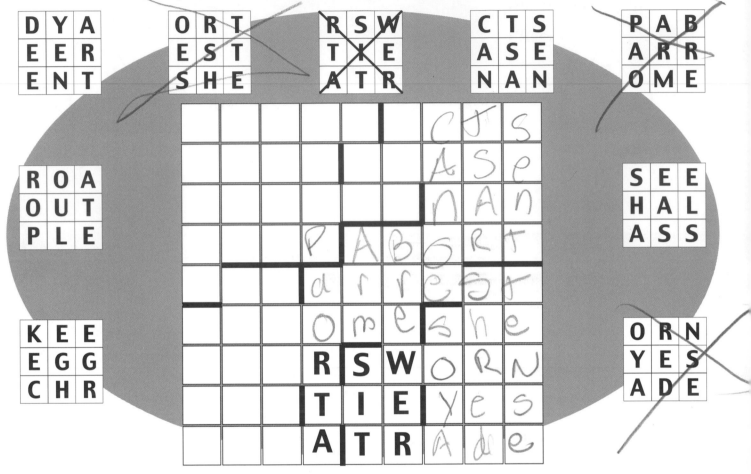

SCRAMBLE

Can you rearrange these letters and make another eight-letter word?

Clue: Gagged

TWINS

16

Pair-up each word in the first circle with a word of similar meaning in the second. When you have finished, one word from each circle will be left without a twin.

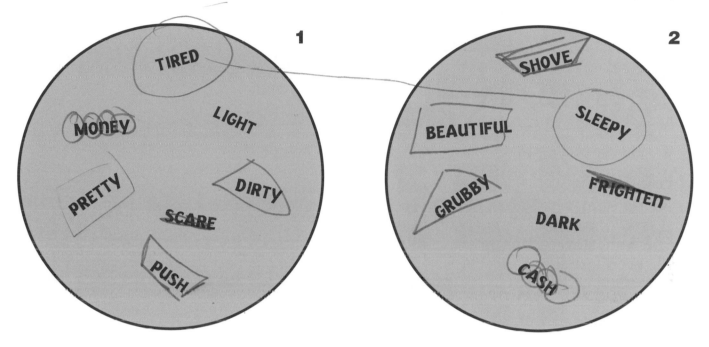

1

TIRED

MONEY

LIGHT

PRETTY

DIRTY

SCARE

PUSH

2

SHOVE

BEAUTIFUL

SLEEPY

GRUBBY

FRIGHTEN

DARK

CASH

ALL CHANGE

17

Rearrange the words in each row to make a new one. Write it in the same line in the second box. Sometimes you will be able to make more than one word, so we have given a clue to help you. Another five-letter word will appear in the shaded column.

R	E	A	C	T
R	E	S	I	N
A	G	R	E	E
A	D	D	E	R
L	E	M	O	N

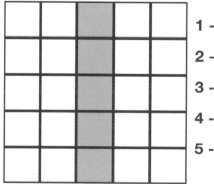

1 - Draw over a line

2 - Clean with water

3 - Keen

4 - Fear

5 - Yellow fruit (another)

Clue: Gods messenger

VOWEL PLAY

All the vowels have been taken out of this crossword and placed in boxes next to the grid. Can you replace them all in their correct positions?

ANAGRAM TIMER

The answer to each of the clues is an anagram of the word above and below it, plus or minus one letter.

1 - Watch band

2 - Famous person

3 - Sewer rodent

4 - Plan to catch someone / something

5 - Social gathering

CHAPTER 2

INCOMPLETE

One of every letter of the alphabet has been taken from this puzzle.
Can you put them all back into their correct positions?

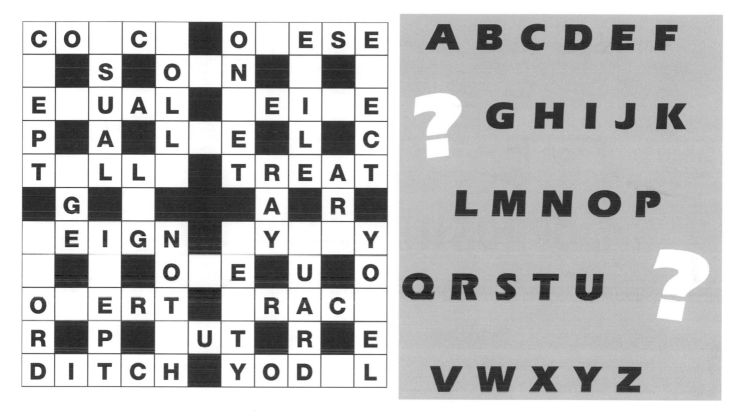

STEP LADDER

By changing one letter each step, turn GOAT to WOOL in three moves.

Target

Young horse

Idiot!

PROVERBS

Here are three very famous proverbs with some missing words.
From the choices we have given you can you complete them all?

He who - - - the piper - - - the tune.

One man's - - - is another man's - - -.

Time and - - - wait for no - - -.

| POISON | TIDE | PAYS | MEAT | CALLS | MAN |

OPPOSITES ATTRACT

Match the four words on the left with a word of opposite meaning on the right.

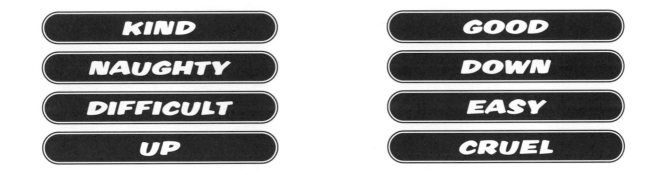

KIND GOOD

NAUGHTY DOWN

DIFFICULT EASY

UP CRUEL

MIX—UP

Unravel the letters to find four countries.

ECFNRA   YEKAN

DAHLNITA   LAIZBR

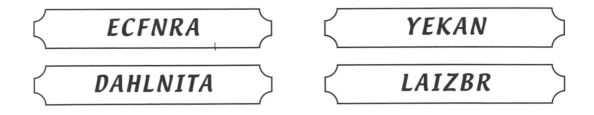
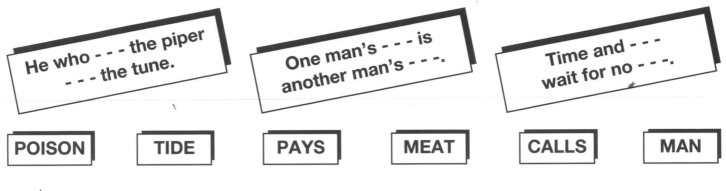

PICTURE THIS

25

Look at each picture carefully and write the initial letter in the corresponding box underneath. When you have finished an eight-letter word will be spelled out.

1	2	3	4	5	6	7	8
D	I	C	T	A	T	O	R

QUICK CHANGE

26

Rearrange the words on each line to make a new word using the clues to help you. Write this new word in the right-hand box and you will discover a new word appearing in the shaded column.

| GROAN |
| ROOST |
| STOAT |
| DREAD |
| SLATE |

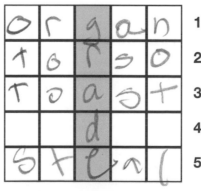

o	r	g	a	n
t	o	r	s	o
T	o	a	s	t
		d		
s	t	e	a	l

1 - Musical instrument

2 - Body trunk

3 - Grilled bread

4 - Venomous snake

5 - Take unlawfully

Clue to hidden word: Mark you get at school.

27

GROUPS

These twelve names of groups of creatures have been mixed up.
Can you re-arrange them into the correct groups?

SIEGE	of	HERMITS
TRIP	of	HARPERS
HUSK	of	LARKS
EXALTATION	of	CRANES
MELODY	of	NIGHTINGALES
OBSERVANCE	of	OWLS
WATCH	of	RABBITS
TRIBE	of	SHEEP
KENNEL	of	HARES
PARLIAMENT	of	GOATS
COLONY	of	RACHES
CRY	of	HOUNDS

TRIANGLE TWINS

Pair-up each word in the first triangle with a word of similar meaning in the second. When you have finished, one word from each triangle will be left without a twin.

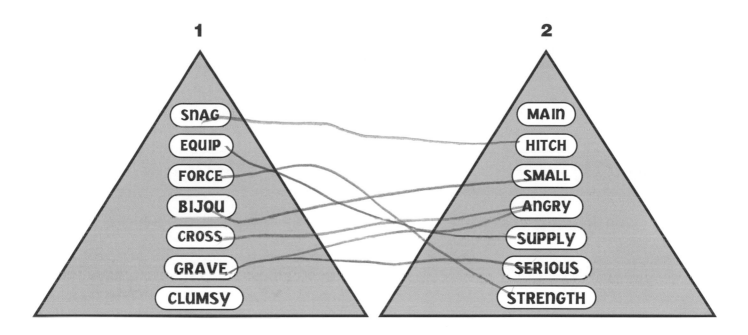

1

- SNAG
- EQUIP
- FORCE
- BIJOU
- CROSS
- GRAVE
- CLUMSY

2

- MAIN
- HITCH
- SMALL
- ANGRY
- SUPPLY
- SERIOUS
- STRENGTH

STAR STRUCK

A letter has been removed from each star and replaced with a question mark. Which letter is needed to complete the word in each shape?
(Clue: A colorful teaser.)

1
L
B A
? C

2
W
O N
? B

3
E
R E
? N

30 # ODDITY

Can you work out which of these words is the odd one out and why?

NO I

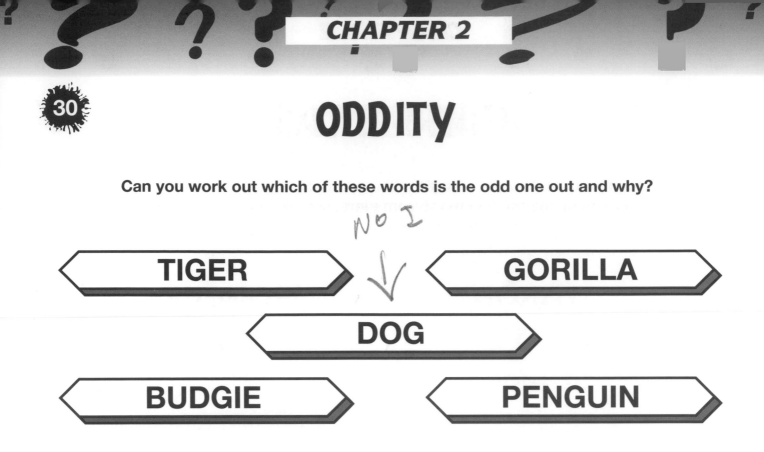

TIGER

GORILLA

DOG

BUDGIE

PENGUIN

31 # DARTBOARD

Fill the shaded segments with one of the five letters below to make four different four-letter words, each reading out from the center.

E L S U W

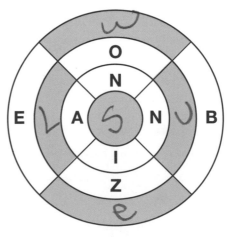

FIRST & LAST

Replace the last letter of each word in column 1, and the first letter of each word in column 2 with the same letter of the alphabet. Put this letter in the middle box to make a new word reading down.

1		2
THROB	W	PONDER
ROTTEN	r	FUNNY
SCAMPS	i	ACE
GUEST	S	TWITCH
WHISK	T	FUNNEL

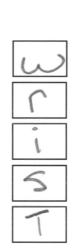

Clue: It joins hands!

LINK UP

Make a new word or phrase by placing the same four-letter word in front or behind each of these words. e.g. Black in front of bird will make blackbird.

- - - - POWDER   OLD - - - -

- - - - DISH   - - - - BUBBLE

- - - - OPERA   - - - - FLAKE

34

ALL MIXED UP

The answers to these clues are given on the right-hand side but the letters have been all mixed up. Can you unscramble them all and solve the puzzles?

1 - Say sorry *Apologize*   **ZIOGLAEPO**

2 - Snooker-like game *Billiards*   **SILBAILRD**

3 - Path for horses *bridalway*   **YEDBRIWAL**

4 - First meal of the day *Breakfast*   **STEAFBKRA**

5 - Simmered meat dish *Casserole*   **SCOLERSAE**

6 - Brought together   **DEOCTLECL**

7 - Listen secretly *eavesdrop*   **PORVEESDA**

8 - Step by step   **ULARDAGYL**

9 - Very strong wind *hurricane*   **INACUHRER**

10 - Listless   **HICGTLEAR**

11 - Precise, exact   **TRACECAU**

12 - Annual celebration *Birthday*   **DIRTBHAY**

ABACUS

35

Slide the abacus beads across the wires to form four birds, reading downwards. All the beads will be used. Keep in mind that the beads are on wires and cannot jump over one another. An empty abacus is provided for you to work in.

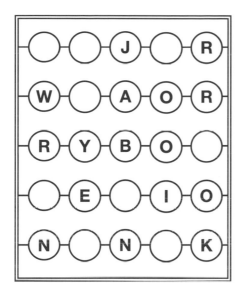

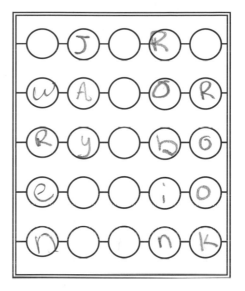

WHAT COMES NEXT?

36

Which of the words below will logically follow on from these?

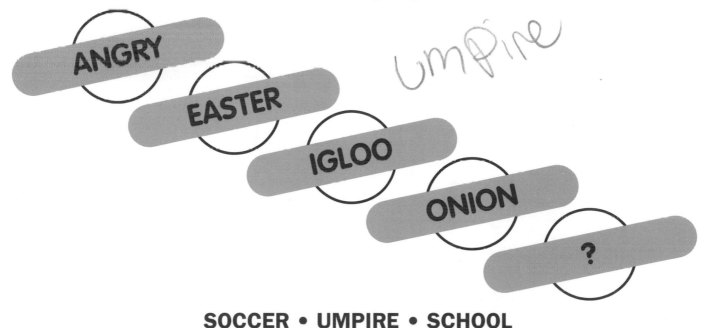

umpire

SOCCER • UMPIRE • SCHOOL

ANAGRAMS

Unscramble the letters in this word to make another one.

S	E	A	S	I	D	E

Clue: Illness, sickness.

BITS 'N' PIECES

Put these blocks of letters back into the grid in the correct order. When complete the grid will show words reading both across and down, separated by a bold line. We have replaced one block and put in the bold lines to help you.

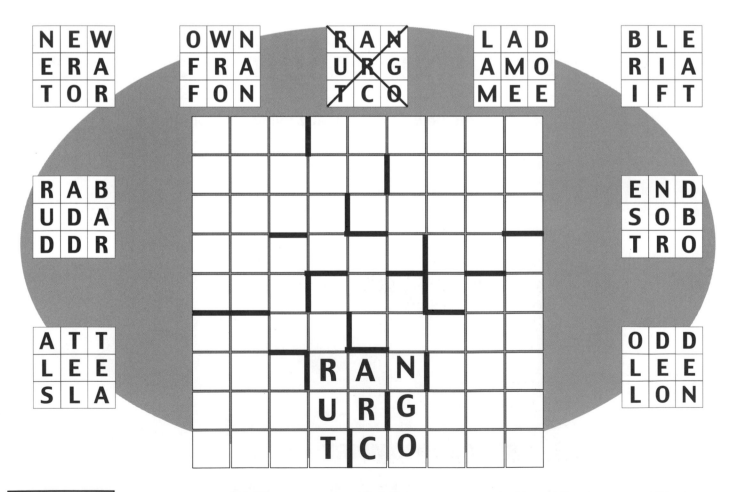

TIME FOR AN ANAGRAM

39

The answer to each of the clues is an anagram of the word above and below it, plus or minus one letter.

1 - Knock over (a drink)

2 - Tablet

3 - Unwell

4 - Accent

5 - Motionless

WHAT NO VOWELS?!

40

We have taken all the vowels out of this crossword and placed them to the right of the grid. Can you replace them all in their correct positions and complete the puzzle?

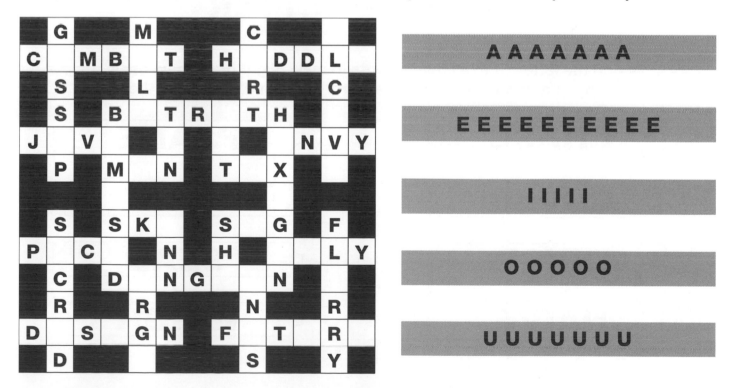

A A A A A A A

E E E E E E E E E E

I I I I I

O O O O O

U U U U U U U

41

HIDDEN WORDS

The name of a European capital city can be found in each of these sentences.
Using your powers of observation see if you can find them all.
e.g. in the following sentence we have hidden the word 'corgi':
Although Mike had changed the de<u>cor, Gi</u>llian still wanted to move house.

1 - When he heard the firework, Amos cowered in the corner.

2 - Even after all the rain we've had, my parasol is bone-dry.

3 - We had fun at the gala, then Sue ruined it by starting a fight.

4 - James was mad, ridiculing the referee like that.

5 - After the paras did the jump a risk assessment was made.

42

ADD—A—LETTER

Add the letter 'T' to all these words to make eight brand new ones.
You can put it at the beginning of the word, at the end, or even in the middle.

CHASE

COVER

DIVER

NAIVE

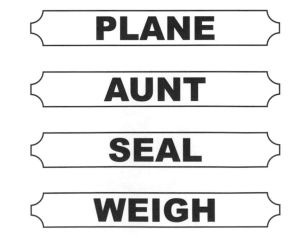

PLANE

AUNT

SEAL

WEIGH

CODEBREAKER

Every letter of the alphabet has been replaced with a number. Your job is to work out which number represents each letter and write it in the grid. We have entered the word NAPE so you know that 12 = N, 17 = A, 24 = P, and 7 = E.
If you get stuck there are two extra letters at the bottom of the page.

1	2	3	4	5	6	7	8	9	10	11	12	13
						E					N	
14	15	16	17	18	19	20	21	22	23	24	25	26
			A							P		

10 = R 26 = L

44

STEP BY STEP

By changing one letter each step, turn FOOT to PARK in three moves.

FOOT				PARK
	Military building	Town with a harbor	Portion	

45

OPPOSITES ATTRACT

Match the four words on the left with a word of opposite meaning on the right.

SHOUT   ANCIENT

HAPPY   WHISPER

INSIDE   SAD

YOUNG   EXTERIOR

46

INSIDE OUT

We have taken a four-letter word out of each of the words listed below. Can you work out which word should go back 'inside' and make a complete word again?
e.g. OVER should go back inside the letters PR - - - - BS to make PROVERBS.

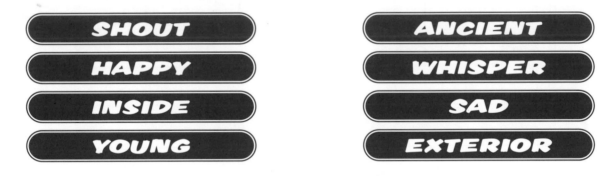

SE - - - - LY   PL - - - - LY   ST - - - - GY

ME - - - - UE   IN - - - - IA   SP - - - - ET

ACID • CURE • RATE • RING • ROCK • SIGN

KEY SEQUENCE

A safe can only be opened by using the keys in the correct order that spells out a word. What is that word? Each key must be used just once.

HECDY

ADD—A—LETTER

Add the same letter to all these words to make a brand new one.
e.g. The letter 't' can be added to moral to make mortal.

BID	**HEAD**
COCK	**TIED**
BEAST	**STAND**
CANE	**TIP**

HIDDEN WORDS

The name of a color has been hidden in each of these sentences.
Can you use your powers of observation and find them all?
e.g. A man's name has been hidden in this sentence: "We hadn't given
up hope terriers would be banned from the dog show next week."

1. If you agree, no one will hear about it.

2. The calm agent asked the way to the embassy.

3. As John dropped the pen in his lap, ink went everywhere.

4. Richard's new job lacked responsibility.

5. The boys took the animal to Ranger Smith, hoping he would

know what to do.

ODD ONE OUT

Which of these animals is the odd one out and why?
(Clue: Think about this at dinner time!)

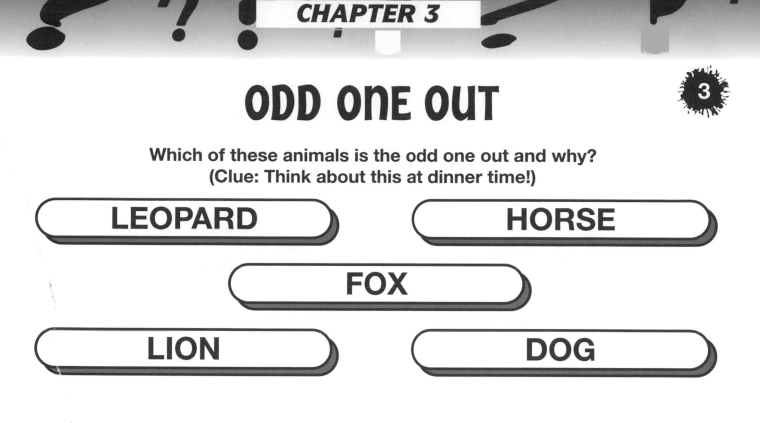

LEOPARD   **HORSE**

FOX

LION   **DOG**

FIRST & LAST

Which letter can replace the last letter of each word in the first column
and the first letter of each word in the second column?
Write your answer in the box in the middle and make a new word going down.

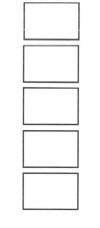

HALT   CUT
SLOT   CLAY
PIT   ITCH
CAT   SING
ROTS   OIL

Clue: Type of musical theater.

CROSSWORD

A regular crossword for you to enjoy. Try working it out by using the clues, but if you get stuck, the answers appear on the bottom of the page in alphabetical order.

ACROSS

1 - Clever, capable (4)
5 - Evening dress (4)
8 - Hair clip (5)
10 - Baby's toy (6)
11 - Shine (6)
12 - Small poisonous snake (5)
14 - Line where two pieces of material are sewn together (4)
16 - Milky-white gemstone (4)
19 - Measure of land (4)
20 - *Home and - - - -*, Australian TV soap (4)
21 - Aid for measuring distances (7)
22 - Plus, as well as (4)
24 - Article on a list (4)
26 - Facial feature (4)
28 - Fly upwards (4)
30 - Association for eggheads! (5)
34 - Doing something (6)
35 - Very happy (6)
36 - A very big person (5)
37 - Pastry with jelly or fruit on it (4)
38 - Area, region (4)

DOWN

1 - Ghostly quality (4)
2 - Part of the alphabet (6)
3 - Toboggan (4)
4 - Lazy (4)
6 - Robin Hood, for example (6)
7 - Oasis singer, - - - Gallagher (4)
8 - Put down noisily (4)
9 - Europe's single currency (4)
13 - Cleaning aid (7)
14 - Small oar (5)
15 - Greek fable writer (5)
17 - Area covered with paving stones (5)
18 - Not now! (5)
23 - Female relative (6)
25 - Drawing on the skin (6)
27 - Fog and smoke mixture (4)
28 - Condiment put on food to enhance the flavour (4)
29 - Something known to be true (4)
31 - *Noddy* author, - - - - Blyton (4)
32 - Despatched (4)
33 - Brim, border (4)

ABLE	GIANT	SALT
ACRE	GOWN	SCULL
ACTION	IDLE	SEAM
ADDER	ITEM	SENT
AESOP	LATER	SEXTANT
ALSO	LETTER	SISTER
AURA	LIPS	SLAM
AWAY	LUSTRE	SLED
DUSTPAN	MENSA	SLIDE
EDGE	NOEL	SMOG
ELATED	OPAL	SOAR
ENID	OUTLAW	TART
EURO	PATIO	TATTOO
FACT	RATTLE	ZONE

WHEEL SPIN

Which letter replaces the question mark and completes the word?

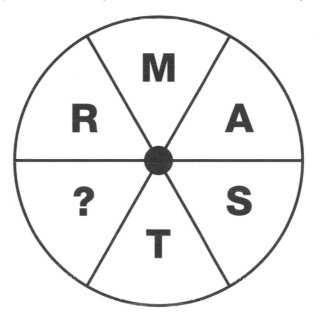

NEXT-IN-LINE

Which of the words below will logically follow on from these?

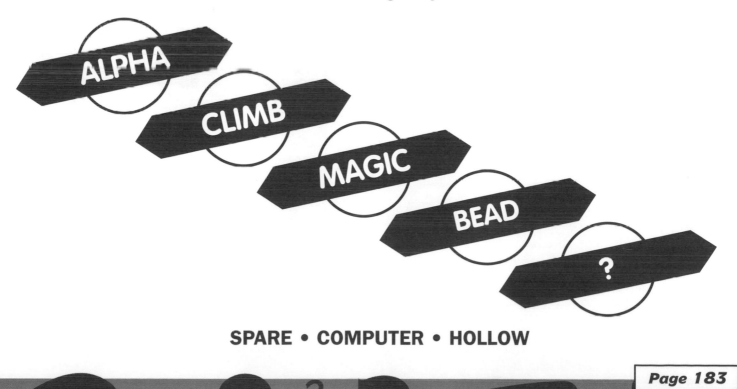

SPARE • COMPUTER • HOLLOW

LINK WORDS

Make a new word or phrase by placing the same six-letter word in front or behind each of these words. e.g. Black in front of bird will make blackbird.

- - - **PLAN**   **PAST** - - -

HEAD - - -   - - - **KEY**

- - - **PIECE**   - - - **MIND**

X - WORDS

Fill in the empty circles and complete the puzzle.
(Clue: Don't look at the shape of the puzzle if you want to be wise!)

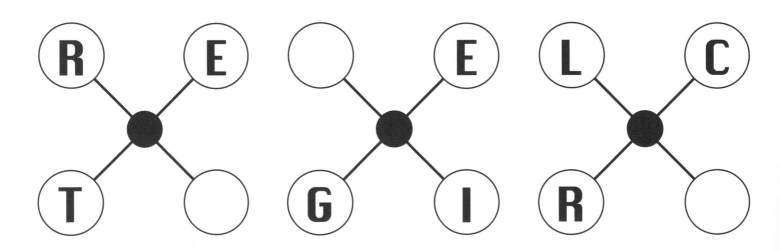

CODEBREAKER

Every letter of the alphabet has been replaced with a number. Your job is to work out which number represents each letter and write it in the grid. We have entered the word PILE so you know that 15 = P, 20 = I, 8 = L, and 17 = E.
If you get stuck there are two extra letters at the bottom of the page.

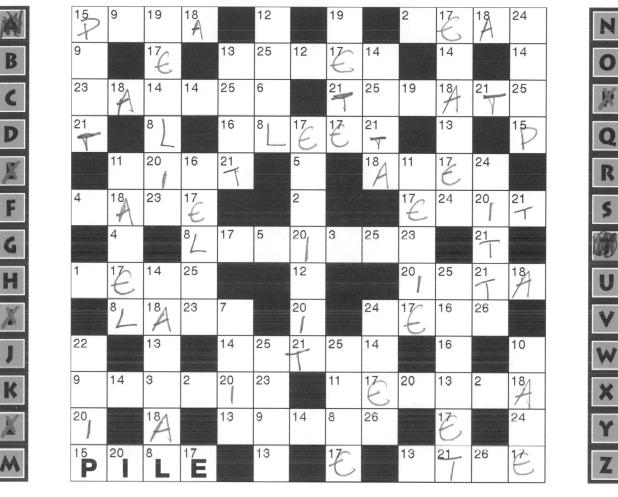

The puzzle grid contains the letter bank A–M on the left and N–Z on the right. The word PILE is filled in at the bottom left (15=P, 20=I, 8=L, 17=E).

Solver's key (bottom reference strip):

1	2	3	4	5	6	7	8	9	10	11	12	13
							L					

14	15	16	17	18	19	20	21	22	23	24	25	26
	P		E	A		I	T					

18 = A   21 = T

11

SCRAMBLED!

The answers to these clues have all been scrambled up. Can you work out what each answer is?

1 NTERUVADE — Exciting experience

2 IARDRERSSEH — Barber

3 ARBELEISM — Very unhappy

4 GIARFEL — Delicate

5 PSANOHTS — Photograph

6 MADNARG — Parent's mother

7 AHEVBE — Be good!

8 TBLALEN — Team game

9 RMAEPTNIS — Chewing gum flavor

10 NCYFA ERSDS — Party costume (5,5)

11 UAEBSEC — For that reason

12 NIELKWR — Skin crease

FIVE STAR

We have taken a letter away from each star and replaced it with a question mark.
Can you work out which letter is needed to complete the word in each shape?
(Clue: Look for something tasty and healthy!)

1

2

3
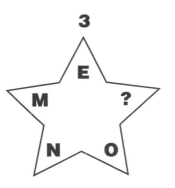

ROGUE WORD

Work out which one of these words
does not belong in this group.

14

JIG-SAW JUMBLE

Put these blocks of letters back into the grid in the correct order. When complete, the grid will show words reading both across and down, separated by a bold line. We have replaced one block and put in the bold lines to help you.

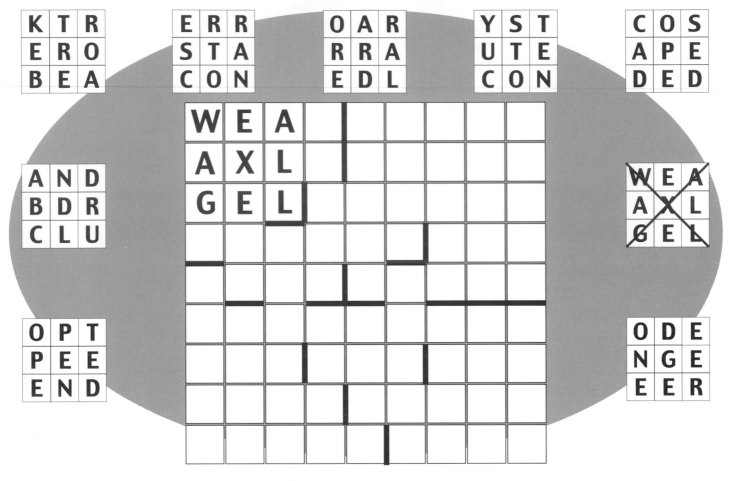

 15

SCRAMBLE

Can you rearrange these letters and make another eight-letter word?

O R I E N T A L

Clue: A family member

TWINS

Pair-up each word in the first circle with a word of similar meaning in the second. When you have finished, one word from each circle will be left without a twin.

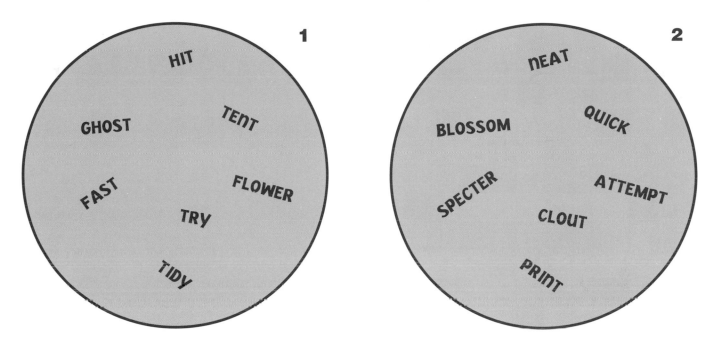

ALL CHANGE

Rearrange the words in each row to make a new one. Write it in the same line in the second box. Sometimes you will be able to make more than one word, so we have given a clue to help you. Another five-letter word will appear in the shaded column.

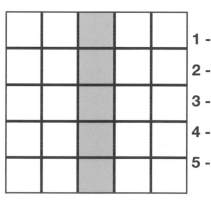

1 - Bicycle part

2 - To light a fire in

3 - A 'group' of mountains

4 - Go over something

5 - Expanse of water

Clue: Move to music

18 VOWEL PLAY

All the vowels have been taken out of this crossword and placed in boxes next to the grid. Can you replace them all in their correct positions?

A A A A A A A A A A A

E E E E E E E E E E E E E E E E

I I I I I I I I I

O O O O O O

U U U U U

19 ANAGRAM TIMER

The answer to each of the clues is an anagram of the word above and below it, plus or minus one letter.

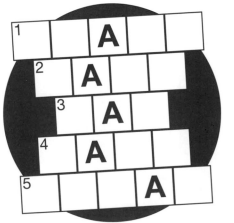

1 - Athletics circuit

2 - Wine bottle holder

3 - Automobile

4 - Speed contest

5 - Unblock

INCOMPLETE

20

One of every letter of the alphabet has been taken from this puzzle.
Can you put them all back into their correct positions?

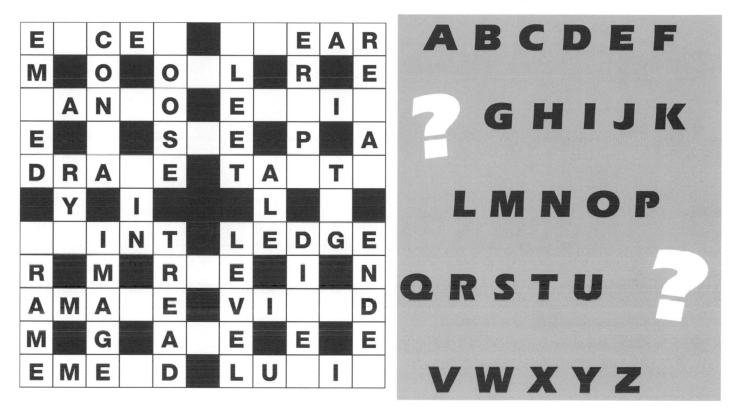

A B C D E F

? G H I J K

L M N O P

Q R S T U ?

V W X Y Z

STEP LADDER

21

By changing one letter each step, turn FIRE to WOOD in three moves.

FIRE

WOOD

Fine metal thread

Was dressed in

Unit of speech

PROVERBS

Here are three very famous proverbs with some missing words.
From the choices we have given you, can you complete them all?

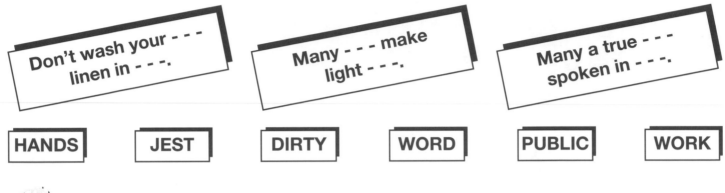

Don't wash your - - - linen in - - -.

Many - - - make light - - -.

Many a true - - - spoken in - - -.

| HANDS | JEST | DIRTY | WORD | PUBLIC | WORK |

OPPOSITES ATTRACT

Match the four words on the left with a word of opposite meaning on the right.

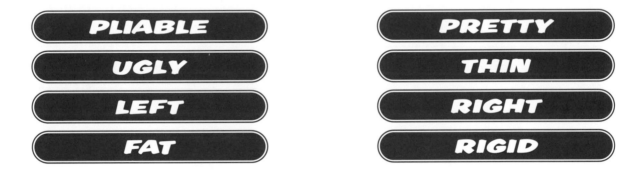

PLIABLE   PRETTY

UGLY   THIN

LEFT   RIGHT

FAT   RIGID

MIX-UP

Unravel the letters to find four months.

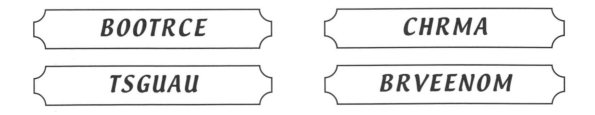

BOOTRCE   CHRMA

TSGUAU   BRVEENOM

PICTURE THIS

25

Look at each picture carefully and write the initial letter in the corresponding box underneath. When you have finished an eight-letter word will be spelled out.

| 1 | 2 | 3 | 4 | 5 | 6 | 7 | 8 |

| G | R | A | N | D | S | O | N |
| 1 | 2 | 3 | 4 | 5 | 6 | 7 | 8 |

QUICK CHANGE

26

Rearrange the words on each line to make a new word using the clues to help you. Write this new word in the right-hand box and you will discover a new word appearing in the shaded column.

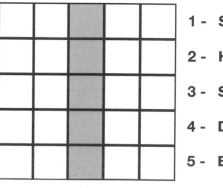

C	A	P	E	R
R	U	N	E	S
N	O	T	E	S
S	H	A	P	E
B	R	A	K	E

1 - Summarise

2 - Hospital worker

3 - Small rock

4 - Distinct period

5 - Bread maker

Clue to hidden word: A frog might give you this answer.

CROSSWORD

A regular crossword puzzle for you to solve. Try working it out by using the clues first, but if you get stuck we have listed all the words you need to finish the puzzle in alphabetical order at the bottom of the page.

ACROSS

3 – Shock, amaze (9)
8 – Descend sharply (4)
9 – Astronaut (8)
10 – Set fire to (6)
13 – Church passageway (5)
14 – Correct (7)
15 – Male offspring (3)
16 – Quarantine (7)
17 – Bed covering (5)
21 – Animal dung (6)
22 – Buy (8)
23 – Strongly against (4)
24 – In another place (9)

DOWN

1 – Testimony (9)
2 – Catapult (9)
4 – Emotionally distressed (5)
5 – Defame (7)
6 – Honest (4)
7 – Spruce (4)
11 – Facial hair (9)
12 – Artificial (9)
14 – Small deer (3)
15 – Digestive organ (7)
18 – Smudge (5)
19 – Gas and coal, for example (4)
20 – Skin disease (4)

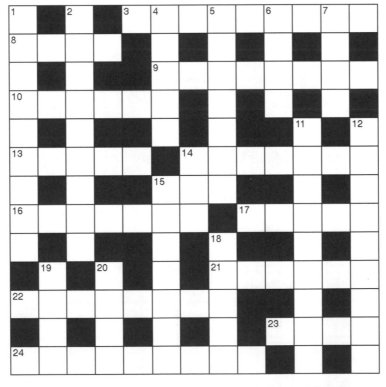

ACNE • AFFIDAVIT • AISLE • ANTI • BLACKEN • DUMBFOUND • ELSEWHERE • FALL • FUEL • IGNITE ISOLATE • MANURE • NEAT • OPEN • PURCHASE • RECTIFY • ROE • SHEET • SIDEBURNS • SLINGSHOT SMEAR • SON • SPACEMAN • STOMACH • SYNTHETIC • UPSET •

TRIANGLE TWINS

28

Pair-up each word in the first triangle with a word of similar meaning in the second. When you have finished, one word from each triangle will be left without a twin.

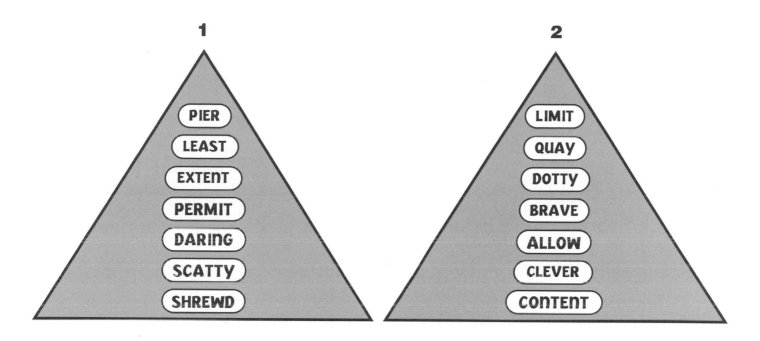

1

PIER
LEAST
EXTENT
PERMIT
DARING
SCATTY
SHREWD

2

LIMIT
QUAY
DOTTY
BRAVE
ALLOW
CLEVER
CONTENT

STAR STRUCK

29

A letter has been removed from each star and replaced with a question mark. Which letter is needed to complete the word in each shape?
(Clue: A meaty puzzle to get your teeth into.)

1

N
O   ?
C   A

2

A
K   E
S   ?

3

O
P   ?
S   C

ODDITY

Can you work out which of these words is the odd one out and why?

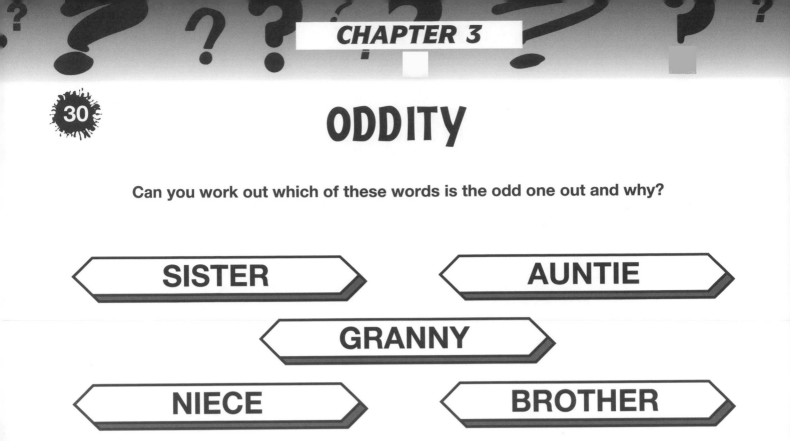

SISTER

AUNTIE

GRANNY

NIECE

BROTHER

DARTBOARD

Fill the shaded segments with one of the five letters below to make four different four-letter words, each reading out from the center.

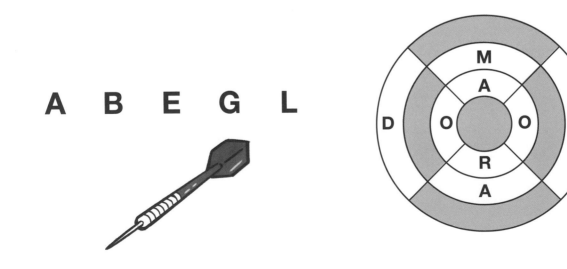

A B E G L

FIRST & LAST

32

Replace the last letter of each word in column 1, and the first letter of each word in column 2 with the same letter of the alphabet. Put this letter in the middle box to make a new word reading down.

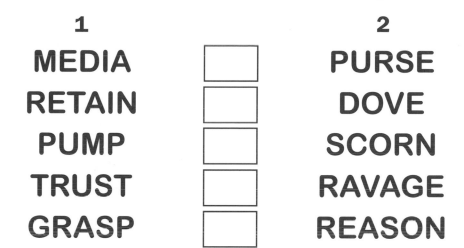

1		2
MEDIA		PURSE
RETAIN		DOVE
PUMP		SCORN
TRUST		RAVAGE
GRASP		REASON

Clue: You will find lots at school!

LINK UP

33

Make a new word or phrase by placing the same five-letter word in front or behind each of these words. e.g. Show in front of boat will make showboat.

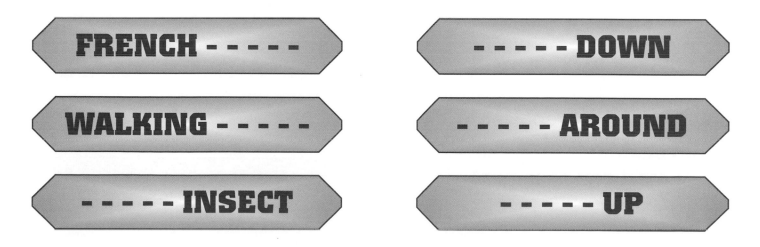

FRENCH - - - - -

- - - - - DOWN

WALKING - - - - -

- - - - - AROUND

- - - - - INSECT

- - - - - UP

ALL MIXED UP

The answers to these clues are given on the right-hand side but the letters have been mixed up. Can you unscramble them all and solve the puzzles?

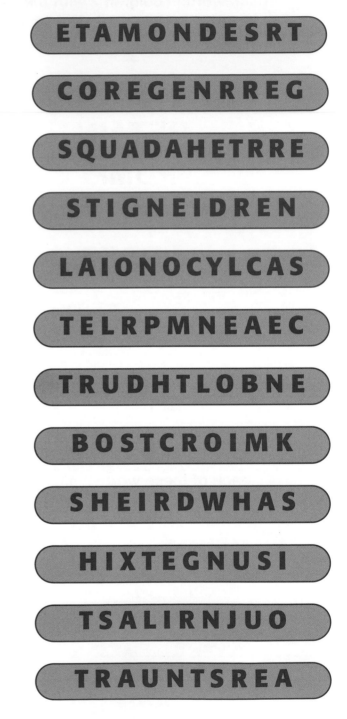

1 - Show in a practical way   ETAMONDESRT

2 - Fruit and vegetable seller   COREGENRREG

3 - Center of operations   SQUADAHETRRE

4 - Items needed for cooking   STIGNEIDREN

5 - Sometimes   LAIONOCYLCAS

6 - Substitute   TELRPMNEAEC

7 - Flash of lightning   TRUDHTLOBNE

8 - Witch's transport   BOSTCROIMK

9 - Appliance for cleaning plates   SHEIRDWHAS

10 - Put out (a fire)   HIXTEGNUSI

11 - Newspaper reporter   TSALIRNJUO

12 - Eating establishment   TRAUNTSREA

ABACUS

Slide the abacus beads across the wires to form four animals, reading downward. All the beads will be used. Keep in mind that the beads are on wires and cannot jump over one another. An empty abacus is provided for you to work in.

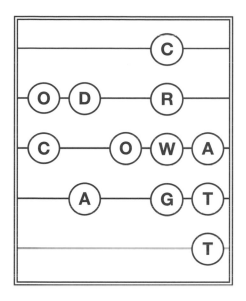

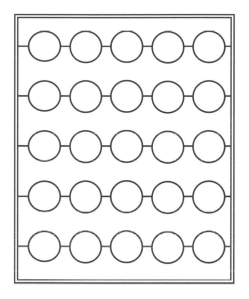

WHAT COMES NEXT?

Which of the words below will logically follow on from these?

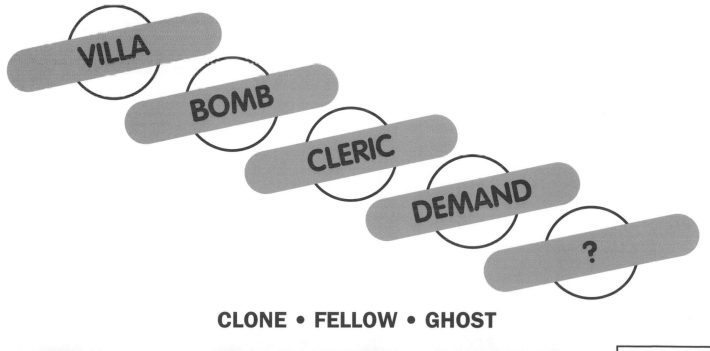

VILLA

BOMB

CLERIC

DEMAND

?

CLONE • FELLOW • GHOST

37 ANAGRAMS

Unscramble the letters in this word to make another one.

| E | N | L | A | R | G | E |

| | | | | | | |

Clue: Army officer.

38 BITS 'N' PIECES

Put these blocks of letters back into the grid in the correct order. When complete the grid will show words reading both across and down, separated by a bold line. We have replaced one block and put in the bold lines to help you.

F I N	L E Y	V A L	O A K	W A D
L D I	I M P	E R A	U S E	S L E
A L L	D I E	L E D	T H R	O S T

| W O E |
| A R C |
| S E T |

| N A P |
| O R A |
| R E C |

| A L E |
| N E R |
| E G O |

| T E A |
| H A S |
| O W H |

TIME FOR AN ANAGRAM

The answer to each of the clues is an anagram of the word above and below it, plus or minus one letter.

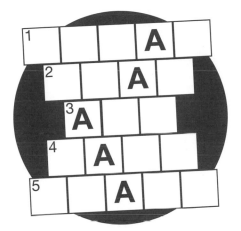

1 - Visage seen in your sleep

2 - Quantity of paper

3 - Upper limb

4 - Sloping platform

5 - Vagrant

WHAT, NO VOWELS!

We have taken all the vowels out of this crossword and placed them to the right of the grid. Can you replace them all in their correct positions and complete the puzzle?

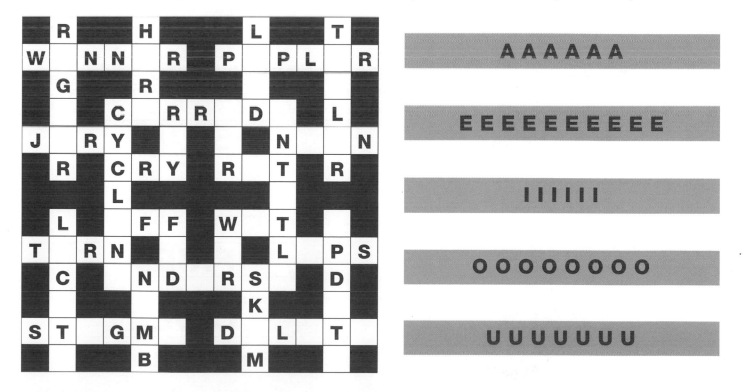

 41

HIDDEN WORDS

The name of a European country can be found in each of these sentences.
Using all of your powers of observation see if you can find them all.
e.g. In the following sentence we have hidden the word 'corgi':
Although Mike had changed the de<u>cor, Gi</u>llian still wanted to move house.

1 - Let's hide if Francesca comes.

2 - Angela's pa injured himself falling off the ladder.

3 - We had to push the jeep or tug a landing craft to safety.

4 - Despite the charges we denied everything.

5 - Neither Oberon or Wayfarer won the horse race.

 42

ADD—A—LETTER

Add the letter 'N' to all these words to make eight brand new ones.
You can put it at the beginning of the word, at the end, or even in the middle.

WADER	**SHUT**
RATIO	**HEAVE**
PRICE	**FRIED**
EARLY	**CIDER**

CODEBREAKER

43

Every letter of the alphabet has been replaced with a number. Your job is to work out which number represents each letter and write it in the grid. We have entered the word **HIDE** so you know that 12 = H, 10 = I, 17 = D, and 5 = E.
If you get stuck there are two extra letters at the bottom of the page.

A B C D E F G H I J K L M

N O P Q R S T U V W X Y Z

22	14	6	6		5		12		16	10	6	7
25			18	13	19	14	10	3	5			5
21			11		14		20		24			26
7	12	5	24		10		18		7	18	13	7
	21				7	10	13				12	
18	2	7	3	18	15		1	25	18	26	21	24
	10			22				5			11	
17	5	8	21	7	5		2	7	5	18	17	15
	3				4	18	7				5	
23	15	3	5		21		3		12 (H)	5	3	23
14			26		25		5		10 (I)			5
9			18	17	4	10	2	5	17 (D)			2
9	21	21	8		5		2		5 (E)	26	10	7

1	2	3	4	5	6	7	8	9	10	11	12	13
				E					I		H	

14	15	16	17	18	19	20	21	22	23	24	25	26
			D									

18 = A 7 = T

STEP BY STEP

By changing one letter each step, turn HEAD to LANE in three moves.

HEAD				LANE
	Heavy metal	Advance, loan	Earth's surface	

OPPOSITES ATTRACT

Match the four words on the left with a word of opposite meaning on the right.

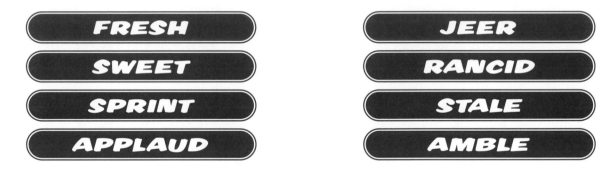

FRESH   JEER

SWEET   RANCID

SPRINT   STALE

APPLAUD   AMBLE

46

INSIDE OUT

We have taken a four-letter word out of each of the words listed below. Can you work out which word should go back 'inside' and make a complete word again?
e.g. OVER should go back inside the letters PR - - - - BS to make PROVERBS.

PR - - - - SS   AP - - - - NT   MA - - - - ES

DE - - - - IC   DI - - - - IC   EN - - - - ED

ABET • CHIN • OGRE • PARE • SPOT • TWIN

MISSING LETTERS

One of each letter of the alphabet has been taken from this crossword grid.
Can you put them all back into their correct positions?

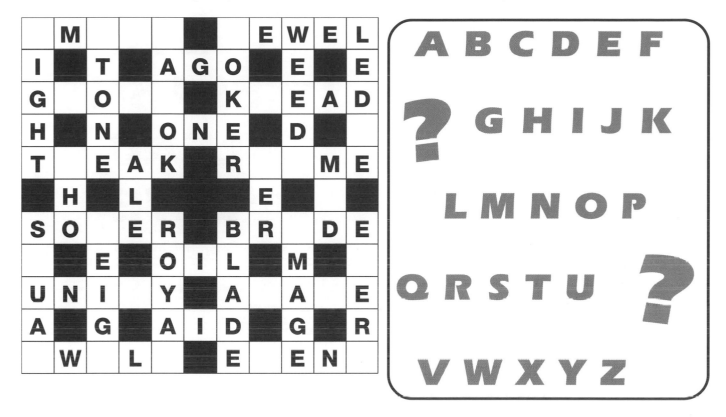

IN A STEW!

Find four games by rearranging the letters in each box.

1	2	3	4
C R O S C E	O K N E S R O	T R I C E C K	Y O K C H E

ADD-A-LETTER

Add the same letter to all these words to make a brand new one.
e.g. The letter 't' can be added to moral to make mortal.

LAY	**SLOE**
LIGHT	**SLASH**
ATCH	**LEAD**
ART	**LATE**

HIDDEN WORDS

The name of a metal has been hidden in each of these sentences.
Can you use your powers of observation and find them all?
e.g. A man's name has been hidden in this sentence: "We hadn't given
up hope terriers would be banned from the dog show next week."

1 - Mike wanted to become a cop, perhaps he liked the uniform.

2 - The wind blew bras, shirts, and jumpers off the line.

3 - You must rest your leg old chap.

4 - Either Munich, Rome, or Paris would get the next Olympics.

5 - I was caught in the wrong place at the wrong time.

ODD ONE OUT

Which of these candies is the odd one out and why?
(Clue: Look at the letters used in each word)

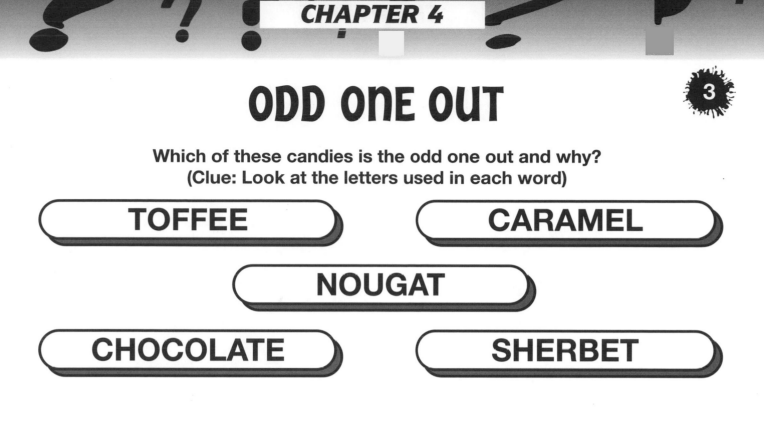

TOFFEE

CARAMEL

NOUGAT

CHOCOLATE

SHERBET

FIRST & LAST

4

Which letter can replace the last letter of each word in the first column
and the first letter of each word in the second column?
Write your answer in the box in the middle and make a new word going down.

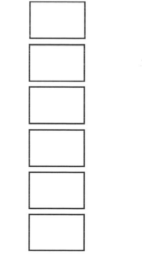

BIN		PEACH
BAT		HIND
SKY		ORE
HOLE		PIMPLE
LET		BONE
MINT		SLOPE

Clue: Use this to cross to the other side.

5

CROSSWORD

A regular crossword for you to enjoy. Try working it out by using the clues, but if you get stuck, the answers appear on the bottom of the page in alphabetical order.

ACROSS

1 - Song from an opera (4)
5 - Every (4)
8 - Higher than (5)
10 - Promise, guarantee (6)
11 - Person in charge of a newspaper (6)
12 - Without anybody else (5)
14 - Animal with a shell, claws, and ten legs (4)
16 - Clean and tidy (4)
19 - Bring up (4)
20 - Fleshy-leaved herb, - - - Vera (4)
21 - Stud or sleeper, for example (7)
22 - A pile of things (4)
24 - Vegetable that tastes like an onion (4)
26 - Old stringed instrument (4)
28 - Hand over for a price (4)
30 - Break or destroy something (5)
34 - Artificial hairpiece (6)
35 - Tiny wave on the surface of water (6)
36 - Very quick (5)
37 - High-pitched sound (4)
38 - Money that you owe someone (4)

DOWN

1 - Slightly open (4)
2 - Take out a policy (6)
3 - Adam and Eve's second son (4)
4 - Place where food can be baked or roasted (4)
6 - Real (6)
7 - Cause injury (4)
8 - Person living in Arabia? (4)
9 - Biblical garden (4)
13 - To shock greatly (7)
14 - Very unkind (5)
15 - Skilled, proficient (5)
17 - Large bird that hunts and eats small animals (5)
18 - Cloth used for drying things that are wet (5)
23 - British word for Fall (6)
25 - Pass by, like time (6)
27 - Large water jug (4)
28 - Slide out of control (4)
29 - Foot movement (4)
31 - Back part of an object (4)
32 - A baby's cot (4)
33 - Opening for fumes to escape through (4)

ABEL	CRUEL	NEAT
ABOVE	DEBT	OUTRAGE
ACTUAL	EACH	OVEN
ADEPT	EAGLE	PING
AJAR	EARRING	RAPID
ALOE	EDEN	REAR
ALONE	EDITOR	RIPPLE
ARAB	ELAPSE	SELL
ARIA	EWER	SKID
ASSURE	HARM	STEP
AUTUMN	HEAP	TOUPEE
BRED	INSURE	TOWEL
CRAB	LEEK	VENT
CRIB	LUTE	WRECK

WHEEL SPIN

6

Which letter replaces the question mark and completes the word?

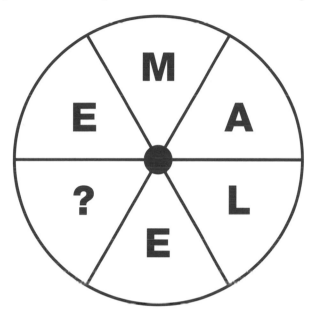

NEXT-IN-LINE

7

Which of the words below will logically follow on from these?

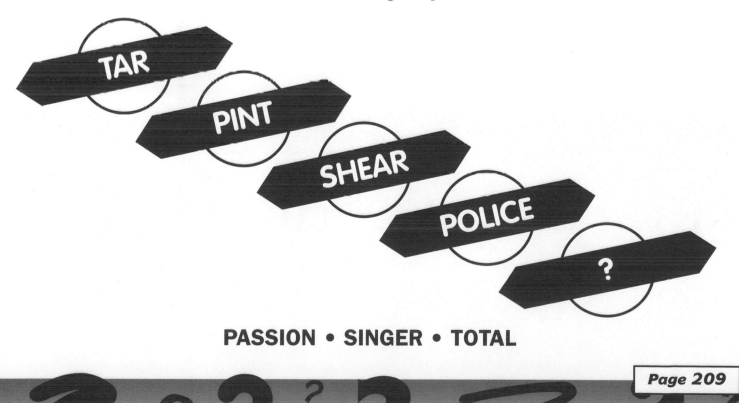

PASSION • SINGER • TOTAL

LINK WORDS

Make a new word or phrase by placing the same five-letter word in front or behind each of these words. e.g. Black in front of bird will make blackbird.

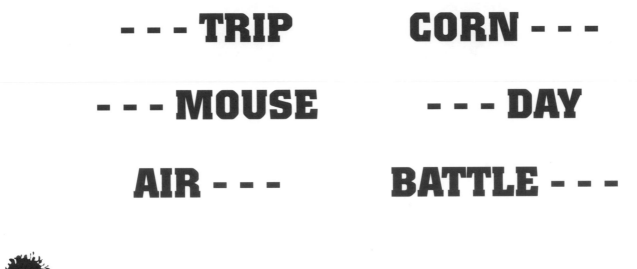

- - - **TRIP**   **CORN** - - -

- - - **MOUSE**   - - - **DAY**

AIR - - -   **BATTLE** - - -

X—WORDS

Fill in the empty circles and complete the puzzle.
(Clue: Don't look at the shape of the puzzle—look for a man's best friend!)

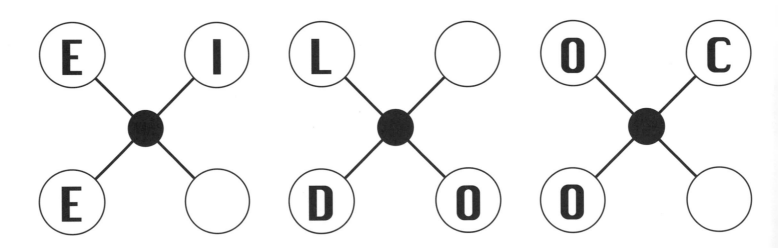

CODEBREAKER

Every letter of the alphabet has been replaced with a number. Your job is to work out which number represents each letter and write it in the grid. We have entered the word URGE so you know that 22 = U, 17 = R, 18 = G, and 14 = E. If you get stuck there are two extra letters at the bottom of the page.

1 = A   21 = L

11

SCRAMBLED!

**The answers to these clues have all been scrambled up.
Can you work out what each answer is?**

1 ANMKEINC   Friendly title

2 TNYRECU   One hundred years

3 NNOEISAYMA   Salad dressing

4 OPTARIR   JFK, La Guardia e.g.

5 BIBHRSU   Trash

6 INRRSPET   Athlete

7 NTACRIU   Window covering

8 OBDRACRAD   Thick paper

9 NESTAB   Not present

10 KEIMAST   Error

11 ERDLWUFNO   Very good

12 ESHOSAER   Beach

FIVE STAR

We have taken a letter away from each star and replaced it with a question mark. Can you work out which letter is needed to complete the word in each shape? (Clue: Look for something you might wear.)

1

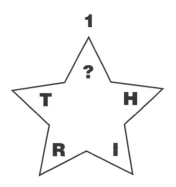

2

3

ROGUE WORD

13

Work out which one of these words does not belong in this group.

14 # JIG-SAW JUMBLE

Put these blocks of letters back into the grid in the correct order. When complete the grid will show words reading both across and down, separated by a bold line. We have replaced one block and put in the bold lines to help you.

E	P	T
M	A	R
B	Y	E

D	O	W
L	O	A
E	N	D

W	A	L
E	N	E
E	N	T

N	A	D
D	C	U
A	T	E

N	U	R
E	L	O
E	S	T

S	E	B
P	E	E
A	T	E

K	A	D
R	G	Y
I	R	E

A	P	T
R	I	O
D	E	N

E	A	M
R	G	O
H	E	R

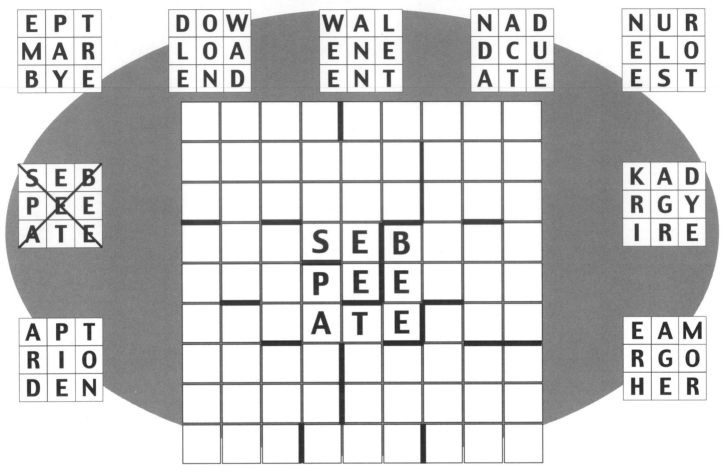

15 # SCRAMBLE

Can you rearrange these letters and make another eight-letter word?

R	E	S	T	R	A	I	N

Clue: Sports shoes

TWINS

Pair up each word in the first circle with a word of similar meaning in the second. When you have finished, one word from each circle will be left without a twin.

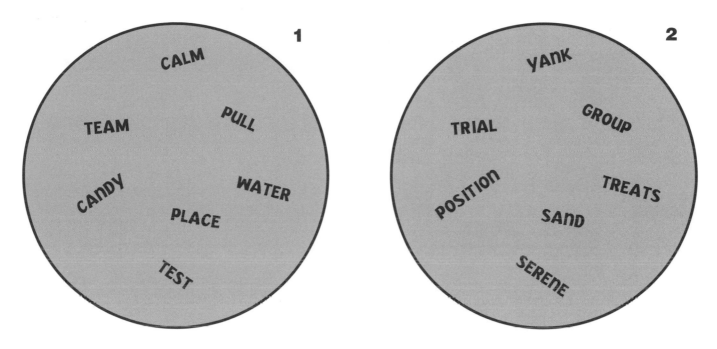

1

CALM
PULL
TEAM
WATER
CANDY
PLACE
TEST

2

YANK
GROUP
TRIAL
TREATS
POSITION
SAND
SERENE

ALL CHANGE

Rearrange the words in each row to make a new one. Write it in the same line in the second box. Sometimes you will be able to make more than one word, so we have given a clue to help you. Another five-letter word will appear in the shaded column.

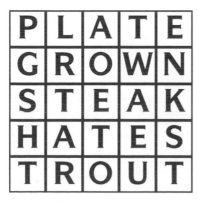

P	L	A	T	E
G	R	O	W	N
S	T	E	A	K
H	A	T	E	S
T	R	O	U	T

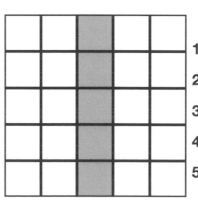

1 - Part of a flower

2 - Incorrect

3 - Pointed stick

4 - Calling for speed

5 - Teacher

Clue: Grilled bread

18

VOWEL PLAY

All the vowels have been taken out of this crossword and placed in boxes next to the grid. Can you replace them all in their correct positions?

19

ANAGRAM TIMER

The answer to each of the clues is an anagram of the word above and below it, plus or minus one letter.

1 - Emulsion or gloss, for example

2 - Gasp for breath

3 - Lightly tap

4 - Measuring device

5 - Part of a flower

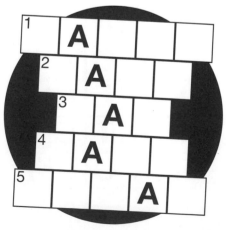

INCOMPLETE

20

One of every letter of the alphabet has been taken from this puzzle.
Can you put them all back into their correct positions?

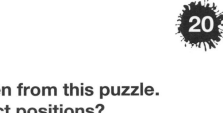

STEP LADDER

21

By changing one letter each step, turn BONE to HEAD in three moves.

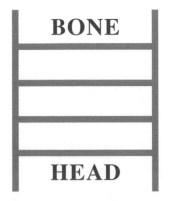

BONE

James, 007

Corner in the road

Necklace decoration

HEAD

PROVERBS

Here are three very famous proverbs with some missing words.
From the choices we have given you can you complete them all?

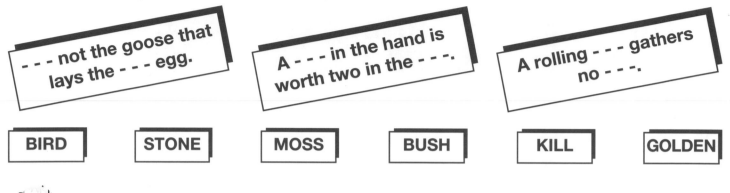

- - - not the goose that lays the - - - egg.

A - - - in the hand is worth two in the - - -.

A rolling - - - gathers no - - -.

| BIRD | STONE | MOSS | BUSH | KILL | GOLDEN |

OPPOSITES ATTRACT

Match the four words on the left with a word of opposite meaning on the right.

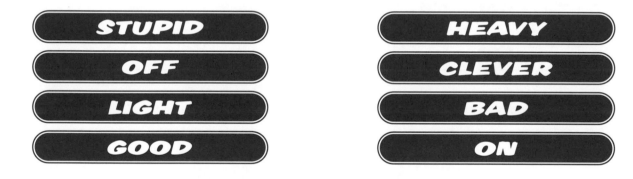

STUPID	HEAVY
OFF	CLEVER
LIGHT	BAD
GOOD	ON

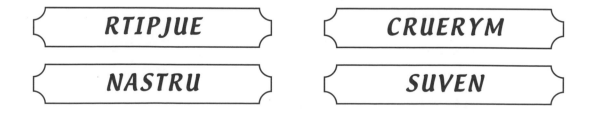

MIX-UP

Unravel the letters to find four planets.

RTIPJUE

CRUERYM

NASTRU

SUVEN

PICTURE THIS

Look at each picture carefully and write the initial letter in the corresponding box underneath. When you have finished an eight-letter word will be spelled out.

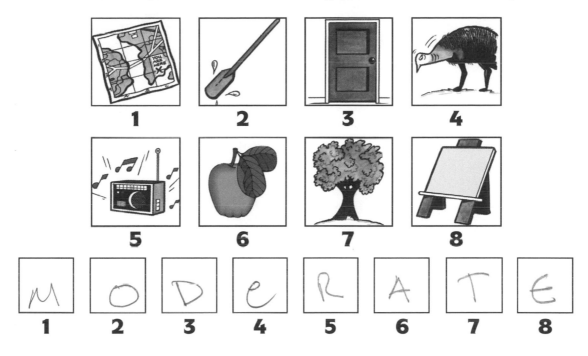

M	O	D	e	R	A	T	E
1	2	3	4	5	6	7	8

QUICK CHANGE

Rearrange the words on each line to make a new word using the clues to help you. Write this new word in the right-hand box and you will discover a new word appearing in the shaded column.

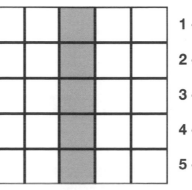

B	R	E	A	M
C	O	R	A	L
F	L	E	S	H
C	R	A	T	E
D	R	A	P	E

1 - Traffic light color

2 - Christmas song

3 - Ledge

4 - Copy through paper

5 - Army clergyman

Clue to hidden word: It's made with dough.

27

CROSSWORD

A regular crossword puzzle for you to solve. Try working it out by using the clues first, but if you get stuck we have listed all the words you need to finish the puzzle in alphabetical order at the bottom of the page.

ACROSS

3 – Catherine wheels, eg (9)
8 – Ripped (4)
9 – Weakened (8)
10 – Pure and virtuous (6)
13 – Short and fat (5)
14 – Sweet red pepper (7)
15 – Rested one's body (3)
16 – Civil court case (7)
17 – Started (5)
21 – Picture made from small
pieces of glass (6)
22 – Suitable for young people (8)
23 – Mature (4)
24 – Keep apart (9)

DOWN

1 – Accumulate (9)
2 – Mechanical
failure (9)
4 – Table of contents (5)
5 – Feat (7)
6 – Portent (4)
7 – Was aware of (4)
11 – Mysterious (9)
12 – Joined together (9)
14 – Tap lightly (3)
15 – Brother or sister (7)
18 – Small fish (5)
19 – Heal (4)
20 – Twelve months (4)

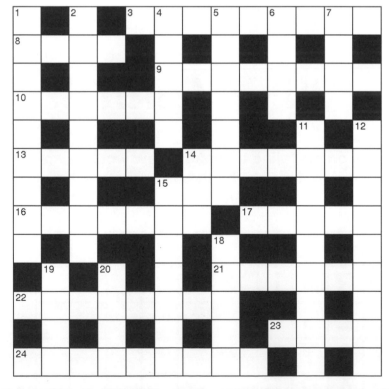

BEGAN • BREAKDOWN • CHASTE • CONNECTED • CURE • DEPLETED • ENIGMATIC • EXPLOIT • FIREWORKS
INDEX • JUVENILE • KNEW • LAWSUIT • MOSAIC • OMEN • PAT • PIMENTO • PODGY • RIPE • SAT • SEGREGATE
SIBLING • SMELT • STOCKPILE • TORE • YEAR

TRIANGLE TWINS

Pair up each word in the first triangle with a word of similar meaning in the second. When you have finished, one word from each triangle will be left without a twin.

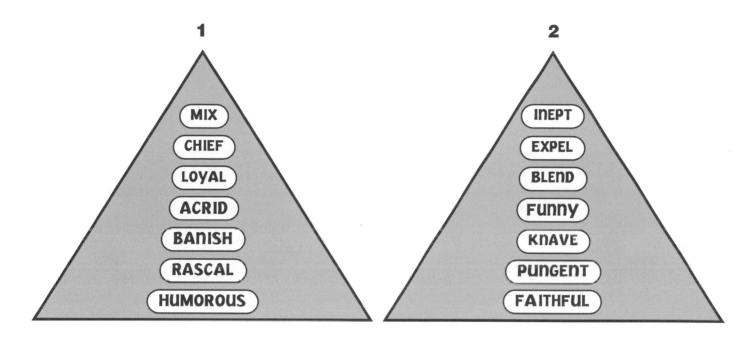

1

MIX
CHIEF
LOYAL
ACRID
BANISH
RASCAL
HUMOROUS

2

INEPT
EXPEL
BLEND
FUNNY
KNAVE
PUNGENT
FAITHFUL

STAR STRUCK

A letter has been removed from each star and replaced with a question mark. Which letter is needed to complete the word in each shape?
(Clue: Open wide.)

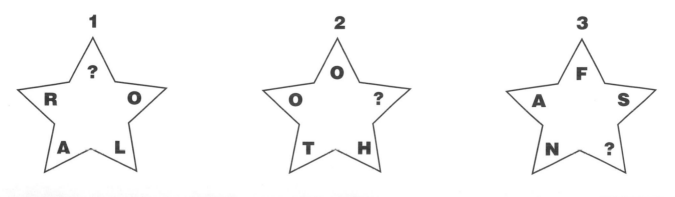

1

?
R   O
A   L

2

O
O   ?
T   H

3

F
A   S
N   ?

30 # ODDITY

Can you work out which of these words is the odd one out and why?

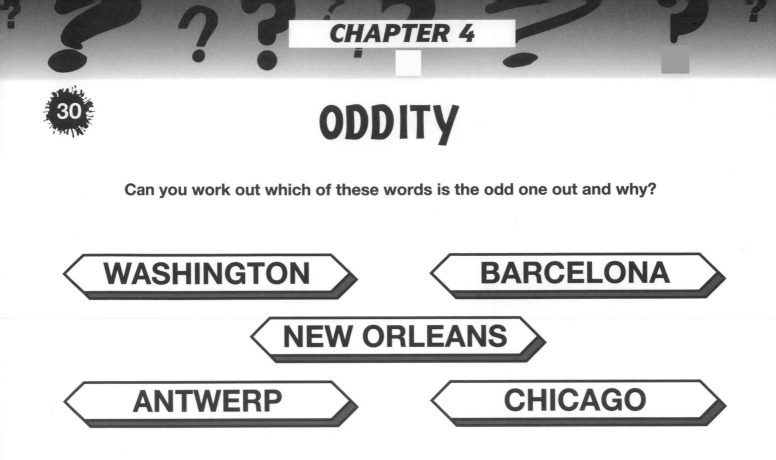

WASHINGTON

BARCELONA

NEW ORLEANS

ANTWERP

CHICAGO

31 # DARTBOARD

Fill the shaded segments with one of the five letters below to make four different four-letter words, each reading out from the center.

A C E N T

FIRST & LAST

Replace the last letter of each word in column 1, and the first letter of each word in column 2 with the same letter of the alphabet. Put this letter in the middle box to make a new word reading down.

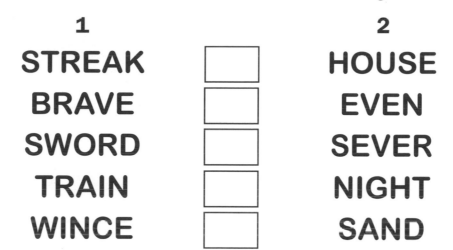

1		2
STREAK	☐	HOUSE
BRAVE	☐	EVEN
SWORD	☐	SEVER
TRAIN	☐	NIGHT
WINCE	☐	SAND

Clue: There are lots in a year.

LINK UP

Make a new word or phrase by placing the same six-letter word in front or behind each of these words. e.g. Show in front of boat will make showboat.

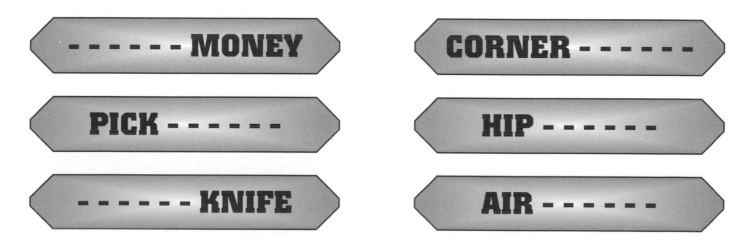

- - - - - - -**MONEY**

PICK - - - - - -

- - - - - - -**KNIFE**

CORNER - - - - - -

HIP - - - - - -

AIR - - - - - -

ALL MIXED UP

The answers to these clues are given on the right-hand side but the letters have been all mixed up. Can you unscramble them all and solve the clues?

1 - Lead from the front

2 - Famous celebrity

3 - Reason to visit the dentist

4 - Carrot or cabbage, for example

5 - Increase speed

6 - Close by, handy

7 - Decorative needlework

8 - Coach, trainer

9 - Throughout the country

10 - Tall building

11 - Non-meat eater

12 - Jobless

HESDAARPE

USRTPSERA

OHEATOCTH

GEVBELEAT

ERELEACATC

VINENOCTEN

REIODYMBRE

TRUIOCNSTR

WDNOITEANI

PRESSCYKAR

NARIEEGVAT

DYOMLENEUP

ABACUS

35

Slide the abacus beads across the wires to form four flowers reading downward. All the beads will be used. Keep in mind that the beads are on wires and cannot jump over one another. An empty abacus is provided for you to work in.

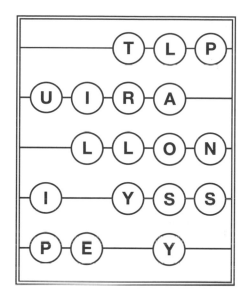

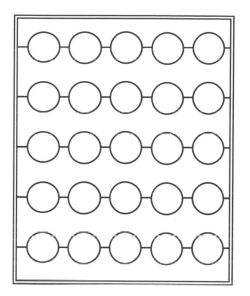

WHAT COMES NEXT?

36

Which of the words below will logically follow on from these?

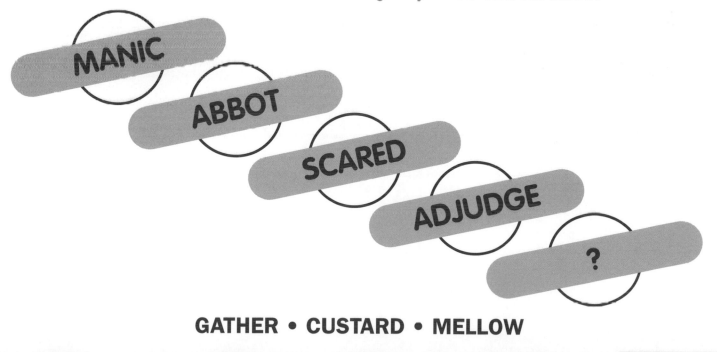

MANIC · ABBOT · SCARED · ADJUDGE · ?

GATHER • CUSTARD • MELLOW

37

ANAGRAMS

Unscramble the letters in this word to make another one.

| R | U | F | F | I | A | N |

| | | | | | | |

Clue: Amusement park.

38

BITS 'N' PIECES

Put these blocks of letters back into the grid in the correct order. When complete the grid will show words reading both across and down, separated by a bold line. We have replaced one block and put in the bold lines to help you.

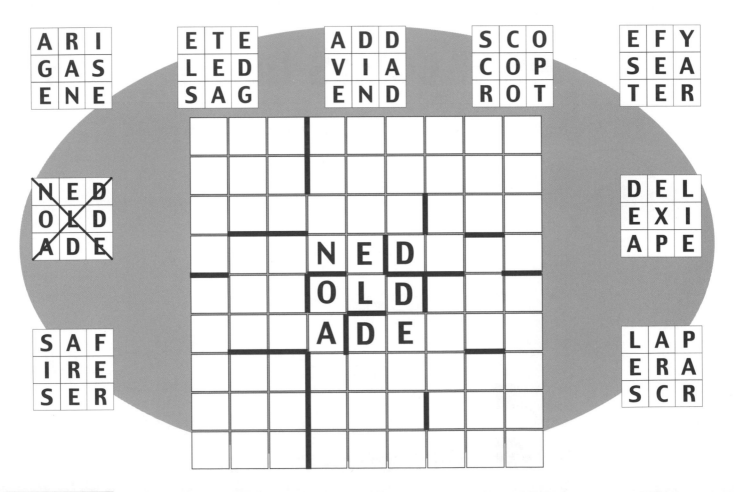

TIME FOR AN ANAGRAM

The answer to each of the clues is an anagram of the word above and below it, plus or minus one letter.

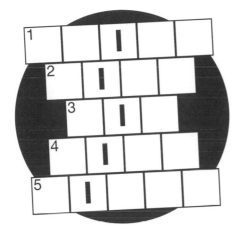

1 - Steps over a fence

2 - Chart, table

3 - Ignited

4 - Roof slate

5 - Supple and athletic

WHAT, no VOWELS!

We have taken all the vowels out of this crossword and placed them to the right of the grid. Can you replace them all in their correct positions and complete the puzzle?

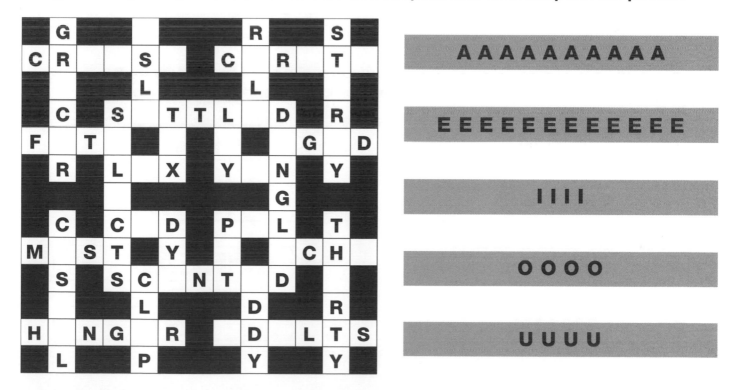

A A A A A A A A A A

E E E E E E E E E E E E

I I I I

O O O O

U U U U

41 HIDDEN WORDS

The name of a material can be found in each of these sentences.
Using your powers of observation see if you can find them all.
e.g. In the following sentence we have hidden the word 'corgi':
Although Mike had changed the decor, Gillian still wanted to move house.

1 - When he finished assembling the cot, Tony had a cup of tea.

2 - At first Sue denied dropping the plate.

3 - After tidying up the garden I managed to wash the car.

4 - I saw Abigail eat her vegetables at dinner time.

5 - The washing line normally gets in the way when Sean plays.

42 ADD-A-LETTER

Add the letter 'D' to all these words to make eight brand new ones.
You can put it at the beginning of the word, at the end or even in the middle.

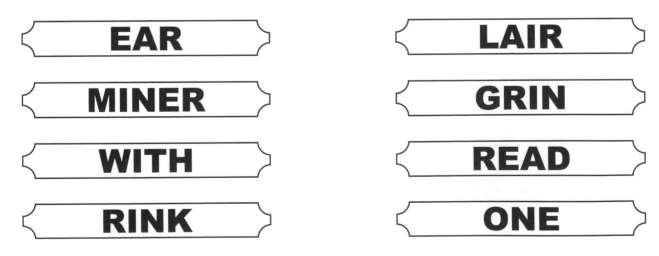

EAR	LAIR
MINER	GRIN
WITH	READ
RINK	ONE

CODEBREAKER

Every letter of the alphabet has been replaced with a number. Your job is to work out which number represents each letter and write it in the grid. We have entered the word LINE so you know that 25 = L, 21 = I, 7 = N, and 22 = E.
If you get stuck there are two extra letters at the bottom of the page.

A B C D E F G H I J K L M

X O P Q R S T U V W X Y Z

24	8	2	25		22		22		2	8	9	2
2			2	7	6	22	25	21	16			16
14			1		6		21		21			4
7	2	20	19		7		15		24	11	3	22
	7				11	23	21				5	
3	26	9	21	7	6		9	2	24	21	8	3
	22			2				16			22	
22	7	11	8	6	4		3	26	11	12	22	9
	7				19	2	13				1	
10	2	9	18		13		11		10	22	22	25
2			22		4		9		2			21
21			22	17	22	16	26	22	24			7
25	22	2	12		7		19		22	24	6	22

1	2	3	4	5	6	7	8	9	10	11	12	13
						N						

14	15	16	17	18	19	20	21	22	23	24	25	26
							I	E			L	

2 = A 3 = S

44

STEP BY STEP

By changing one letter each step, turn FARE to ROAM in three moves.

FARE				ROAM
	Agriculture center	Type, kind	Cushion material	

 45

OPPOSITES ATTRACT

Match the four words on the left with a word of opposite meaning on the right.

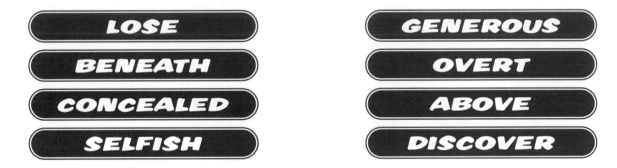

LOSE

BENEATH

CONCEALED

SELFISH

GENEROUS

OVERT

ABOVE

DISCOVER

 46

INSIDE OUT

We have taken a four-letter word out of each of the words listed below. Can you work out which word should go back 'inside' and make a complete word again?
e.g. OVER should go back inside the letters PR - - - - BS to make PROVERBS.

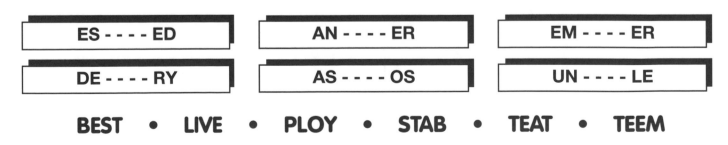

ES - - - - ED	AN - - - - ER	EM - - - - ER
DE - - - - RY	AS - - - - OS	UN - - - - LE

BEST • LIVE • PLOY • STAB • TEAT • TEEM

MISSING LETTERS

47

One of each letter of the alphabet has been taken from this crossword grid.
Can you put them all back into their correct positions?

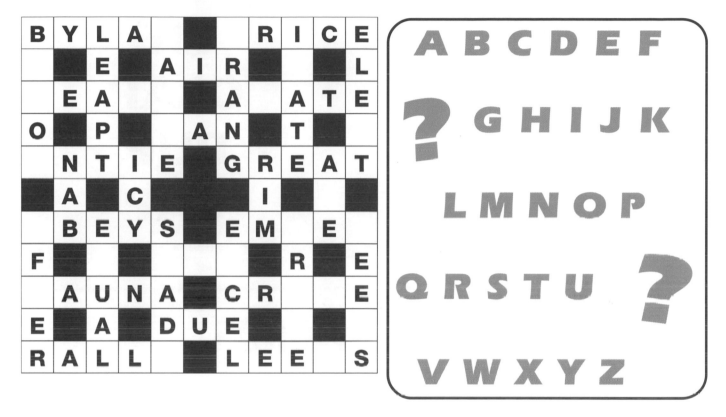

IN A STEW!

48

Find four cheeses by rearranging the letters in each box.

1   2   3   4

ADD-A-LETTER

Add the same letter to all these words to make a brand new one.
e.g. The letter 't' can be added to moral to make mortal.

PAL	**TIE**
LIP	**CLAP**
ORE	**PUP**
EAT	**CAP**

HIDDEN WORDS

The name of a fish has been hidden in each of these sentences.
Can you use your powers of observation and find them all?
e.g. A man's name has been hidden in this sentence: 'We hadn't given
up hope terriers would be banned from the dog show next week.'

1. Try a different route to get home today.

2. Of all the different nuts, almonds are my favorite.

3. It was a super church service on Sunday.

4. Hannah often cheers for her team.

5. Sally lost her ring at the circus last week.

ODD ONE OUT

3

Which word is the odd one out and why?
(Clue: The key is to look for the obvious here!)

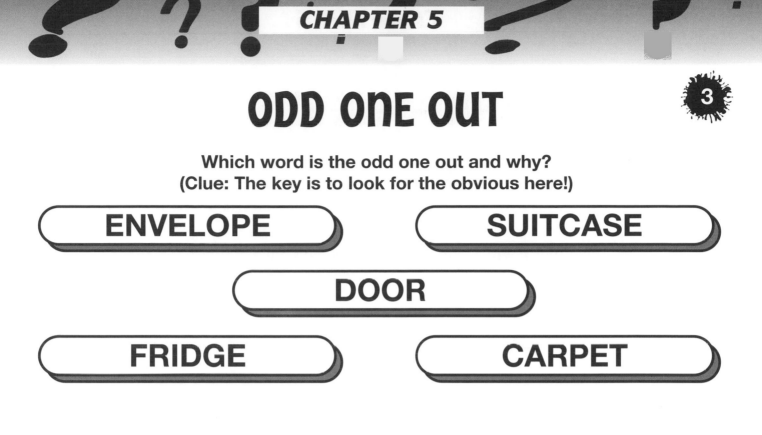

ENVELOPE   SUITCASE

DOOR

FRIDGE   CARPET

FIRST & LAST

4

Which letter can replace the last letter of each word in the first column
and the first letter of each word in the second column?
Write your answer in the box in the middle and make a new word going down.

FORT		COUNT
EGG		PINK
GOOD		LIGHT
CHILL		CREAM
MEDIC		GROUND
CLAP		BELL

Clue: There's lots in each year!

5

PAIR WORDS

Below are two lists of words.
In List A each word has two possible pair words in List B.
In List B each word has two possible pair words in List A.
There are two possible solutions.
Pair a word from each list until you have 10 pairs.

List A	List B
SEVERN	TRACTOR
ARROW	RIVER
TURRET	BULLS-EYE
FARM	BOW
YARBOROUGH	TANK
SAND	CARDS
YEW	CASTLE
VEHICLE	BANK
RIPARIAN	WOOD
JACK	BRIDGE

WHEEL SPIN

6

Which letter replaces the question mark and completes the word?

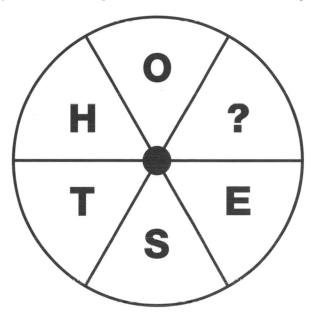

NEXT—IN—LINE

7

Which of the words below will logically follow on from these?

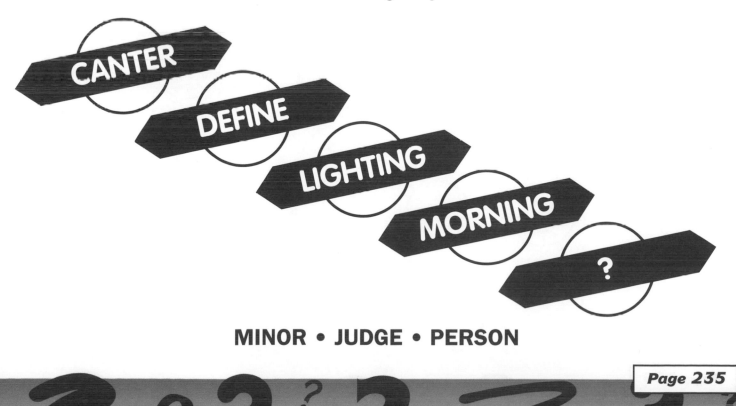

CANTER

DEFINE

LIGHTING

MORNING

?

MINOR • JUDGE • PERSON

LINK WORDS

Make a new word or phrase by placing the same seven-letter word in front or behind each of these words. e.g. Black in front of bird will make blackbird.

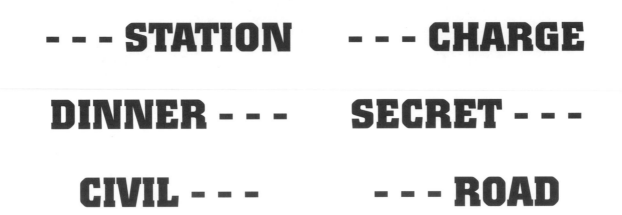

- - - **STATION**   - - - **CHARGE**

DINNER - - -   **SECRET** - - -

CIVIL - - -   - - - **ROAD**

X - WORDS

Fill in the empty circles and complete the puzzle.
(Clue: This could be more colorful than the rest—but a bit trickier!)

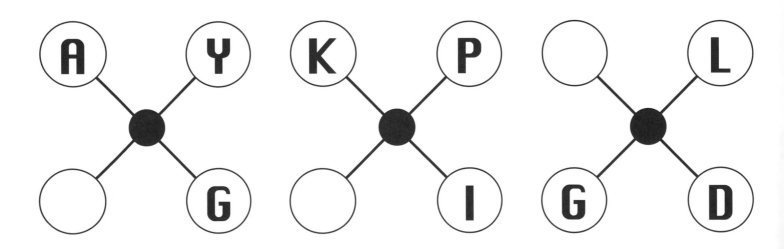

CODEBREAKER

10

Every letter of the alphabet has been replaced with a number. Your job is to work out which number represents each letter and write it in the grid. We have entered the word ITEM so you know that 9 = I, 5 = T, 23 = E, and 11 = M.
If you get stuck there are two extra letters at the bottom of the page.

1	2	3	4	5	6	7	8	9	10	11	12	13
				T				I		M		

14	15	16	17	18	19	20	21	22	23	24	25	26
									E			

18 = R   25 = A

11

SCRAMBLED!

**The answers to these clues have all been scrambled up.
Can you work out what each answer is?**

1 **HTGONIN** Nil

2 **TNTDSIE** Tooth doctor

3 **RYEFWAE** Major road

4 **OTONARC** Humorous drawing

5 **IRFTSLO** Flower seller, arranger

6 **ANTLEGERC** Oblong

7 **ERTSACS** Female performer

8 **ALARESCOT** Moving staircase

9 **ETPYRT** Nice-looking

10 **LILNOSAT** Male horse

11 **ARBRIRE** Fence

12 **RATNATSREU** Eating establishment

FIVE STAR

12

We have taken a letter away from each star and replaced it with a question mark. Can you work out which letter is needed to complete the word in each shape?
(Clue: Some 'body' might help you.)

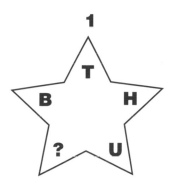

1

2

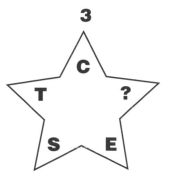

3

ROGUE WORD

13

Work out which one of these words does not belong in this group.

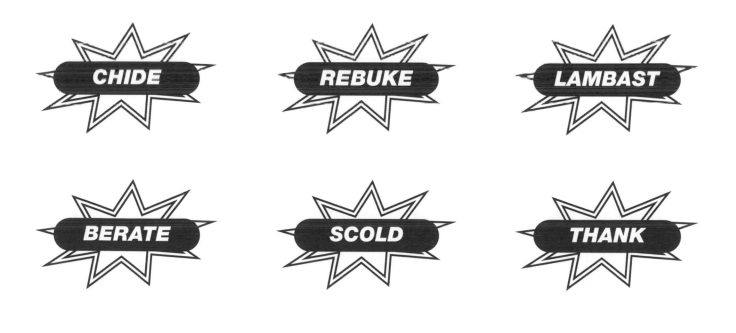

CHIDE

REBUKE

LAMBAST

BERATE

SCOLD

THANK

14

JIG—SAW JUMBLE

Put these blocks of letters back into the grid in the correct order. When complete the grid will show words reading both across and down, separated by a bold line. We have replaced one block and put in the bold lines to help you.

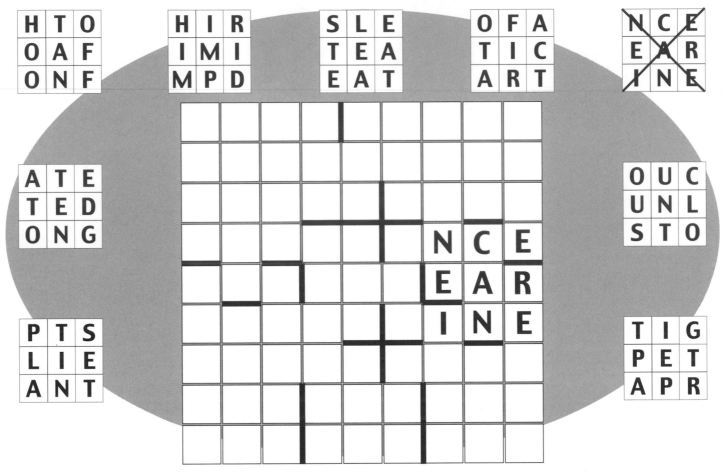

15

SCRAMBLE

Can you rearrange these letters and make another eight-letter word?

U N D E R D O G

Clue: Punishment for being bad

TWINS

Pair-up each word in the first circle with a word of similar meaning in the second. When you have finished, one word from each circle will be left without a twin.

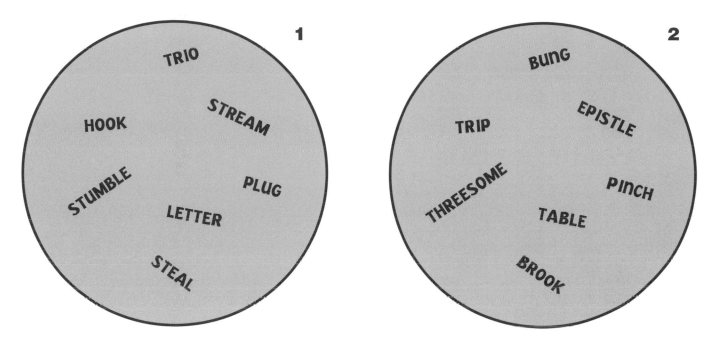

1

TRIO
STREAM
HOOK
PLUG
STUMBLE
LETTER
STEAL

2

BUNG
EPISTLE
TRIP
PINCH
THREESOME
TABLE
BROOK

ALL CHANGE

Rearrange the words in each row to make a new one. Write it in the same line in the second box. Sometimes you will be able to make more than one word, so we have given a clue to help you. Another five-letter word will appear in the shaded column.

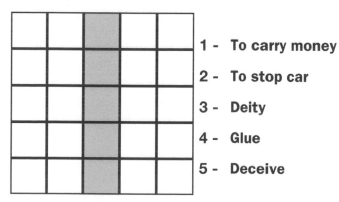

S	U	P	E	R
B	A	K	E	R
S	A	T	I	N
S	P	A	T	E
T	E	A	C	H

1 - To carry money

2 - To stop car

3 - Deity

4 - Glue

5 - Deceive

Clue: Lift up

VOWEL PLAY

All the vowels have been taken out of this crossword and placed in boxes next to the grid. Can you replace them all in their correct positions?

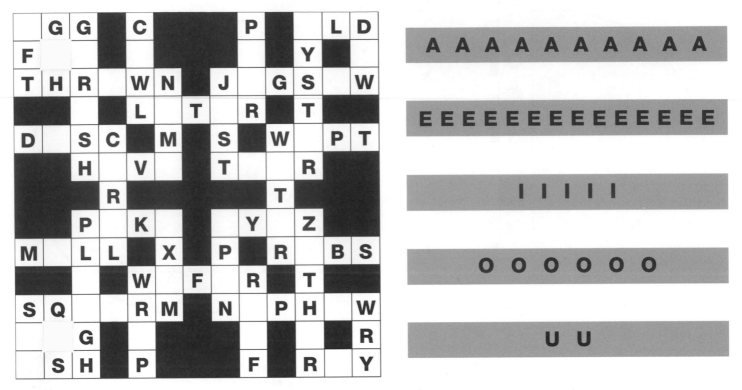

ANAGRAM TIMER

The answer to each of the clues is an anagram of the word above and below it, plus or minus one letter.

1 - Amount paid for something

2 - Metal structure on seashore

3 - Pastry dish

4 - Ready for eating

5 - Church steeple

INCOMPLETE

One of every letter of the alphabet has been taken from ths puzzle.
Can you put them all back into their correct positions?

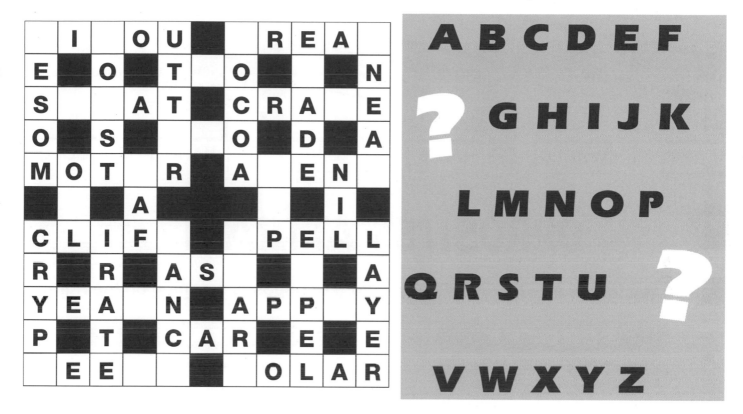

STEP LADDER

By changing one letter each step, turn GLAD to FOOL in three moves.

Provoke

Target

Young horse

PROVERBS

22

Here are three very famous proverbs with some missing words.
From the choices we have given you, can you complete them all?

The - - - that rocks the cradle rules the - - -.

Revenge is a - - - best served - - -.

- - - in - - -, and repent in leisure.

MARRY   WORLD   HASTE   DISH   HAND   COLD

OPPOSITES ATTRACT

23

Match the four words on the left with a word of opposite meaning on the right.

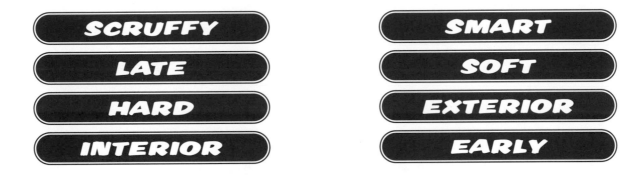

SCRUFFY   SMART

LATE   SOFT

HARD   EXTERIOR

INTERIOR   EARLY

MIX-UP

Unravel the letters to find four items of furniture.

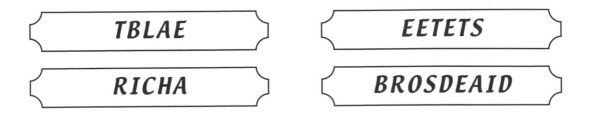

TBLAE   EETETS

RICHA   BROSDEAID

PICTURE THIS

Look at each picture carefully and write the initial letter in the corresponding box underneath. When you have finished an eight-letter word will be spelt out.

P	U	r	C	H	A	S	C
1	2	3	4	5	6	7	8

QUICK CHANGE

Rearrange the words on each line to make a new word using the clues to help you. Write this new word in the right-hand box and you will discover a new word appearing in the shaded column.

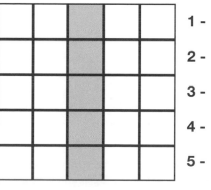

P	A	R	T	S
T	R	A	I	L
T	H	I	N	G
T	H	E	R	E
A	L	E	R	T

1 - Watch band

2 - Court case

3 - Period of darkness

4 - Old anaesthetic

5 - Make different

Clue to hidden word: The correct answer is correct.

CROSSWORD

A regular crossword puzzle for you to solve. Try working it out by using the clues first, but if you get stuck we have listed all the words you need to finish the puzzle in alphabetical order at the bottom of the page.

ACROSS

3 – Hospital (9)
8 – Untainted (4)
9 – Clear soup (8)
10 – Grasp firmly (6)
13 – Mass of bees (5)
14 – Fabric, cloth (7)
15 – Unhappy (3)
16 – Cutting tooth (7)
17 – Blaspheme (5)
21 – Lethargy (6)
22 – Hole in a tire (8)
23 – Transmitted (4)
24 – Everlasting (9)

DOWN

1 – Astronaut's craft (9)
2 – Self–employed (9)
4 – Shallow recess (5)
5 – Disregarded (7)
6 – Cry of a cat (4)
7 – Sleeping policeman (4)
11 – Thrown into disorder (9)
12 – Famous person (9)
14 – Pitch (3)
15 – Short stay (7)
18 – Earthenware beer mug (5)
19 – Deceive (4)
20 – Trick (4)

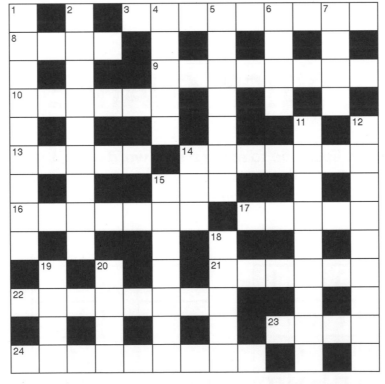

CELEBRITY • CLENCH • CONSOMME • CURSE • DISRUPTED • DUPE • FREELANCE • IGNORED • INCISOR
INFIRMARY • MEOW • NICHE • PERMANENT • PUNCTURE • PURE • RAMP • SAD • SCAM • SENT
SOJOURN • SPACESHIP • STEIN • SWARM • TAR • TEXTILE • TORPOR

TRIANGLE TWINS

Pair-up each word in the first triangle with a word of similar meaning in the second.
When you have finished, one word from each triangle will be left without a twin.

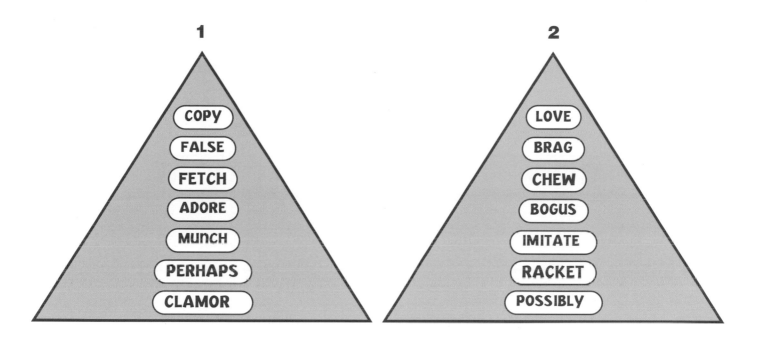

1

COPY
FALSE
FETCH
ADORE
MUNCH
PERHAPS
CLAMOR

2

LOVE
BRAG
CHEW
BOGUS
IMITATE
RACKET
POSSIBLY

STAR STRUCK

A letter has been removed from each star and replaced with a question mark.
Which letter is needed to complete the word in each shape?
(Clue: It's a bit funny this one.)

1

A
R   E
?   G

2

?
L   A
P   E

3

C
A   ?
H   E

30 # ODDITY

Can you work out which of these words is the odd one out and why?
Clue: If you get stuck, try asking the milkman to help you!

SHEEP

BUFFALO

CAT

COW

GOAT

31 # DARTBOARD

Fill the shaded segments with one of the five letters below to make four different
four-letter words, each reading out from the center.

B L N S T

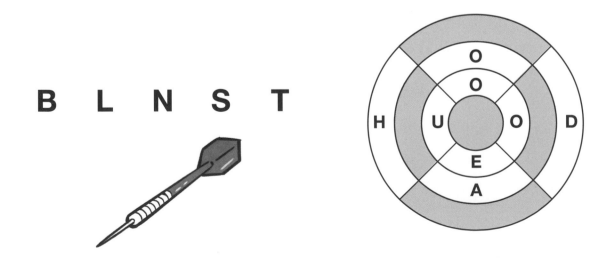

FIRST & LAST

Replace the last letter of each word in column 1, and the first letter of each word in column 2 with the same letter of the alphabet. Put this letter in the middle box to make a new word reading down.

1		2
CLASP		CURRY
COLD		GROUSE
CHIME		JACKET
SWEET		MUZZLE
SUPPLE		BEAR

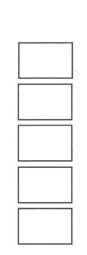

Clue: Cheerful.

LINK UP

Make a new word or phrase by placing the same seven-letter word in front or behind each of these words. e.g. Show in front of boat will make showboat.

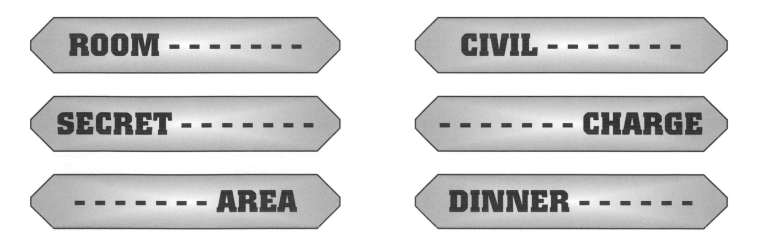

ROOM - - - - - - - -   CIVIL - - - - - - - -

SECRET - - - - - - - -   - - - - - - - - CHARGE

- - - - - - - - AREA   DINNER - - - - - - - -

ALL MIXED UP

The answers to these clues are given on the right-hand side but the letters have been all mixed up. Can you unscramble them all and solve the clues?

1 - Shuttlecock game   T O N B D A I M N

2 - Part played by an actor   C R E A C T R H A

3 - Champion's opponent   N E C T O D N R E

4 - In another place   S E H L E W R E E

5 - Study of the Earth's features   P H A G R E O G Y

6 - Exactly alike   C I A L N E D I T

7 - Very profitable   V A R T L C U I E

8 - Route planner   I R A V G N A O T

9 - Highly trained ambulanceperson   C R A A M P E I D

10 - Know by sight   S I G O N R E C E

11 - Physics expert, for example   S T I N E C T I S

12 - Month of the year   R T E E M P B S E

ABACUS

Slide the abacus beads across the wires to form four numbers reading downward. All the beads will be used. Keep in mind that the beads are on wires and cannot jump over one another. An empty abacus is provided for you to work in.

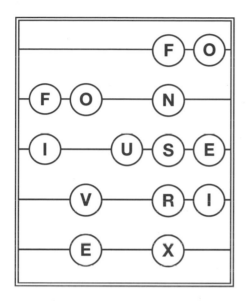

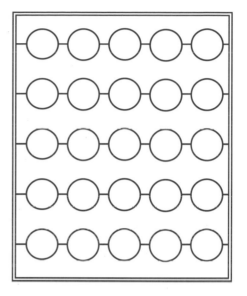

WHAT COMES NEXT?

Which of the words below will logically follow on from these?

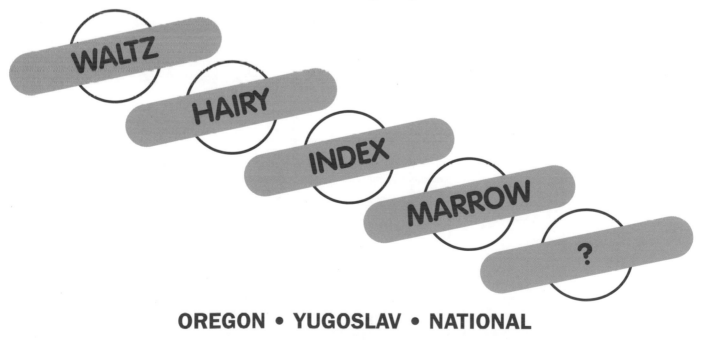

OREGON • YUGOSLAV • NATIONAL

ANAGRAMS

Unscramble the letters in this word to make another one.

H	E	C	T	A	R	E

Clue: Tutor.

BITS 'N' PIECES

Put these blocks of letters back into the grid in the correct order. When complete the grid will show words reading both across and down, separated by a bold line. We have replaced one block and put in the bold lines to help you.

TIME FOR AN ANAGRAM

39

The answer to each of the clues is an anagram of the word above and below it, plus or minus one letter.

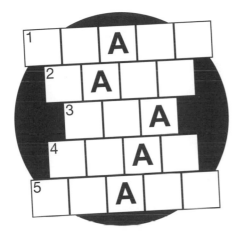

1 - Run after

2 - Container

3 - Body of water

4 - Aquatic creature

5 - Guides

WHAT, NO VOWELS?!

40

We have taken all the vowels out of this crossword and placed them to the right of the grid. Can you replace them all in their correct positions and complete the puzzle?

A A A

E E E E E E E E E E E E E E

I I I I I I I I I I

O O O O O O O O O O

U U U U U U

41

HIDDEN WORDS

The name of a vehicle can be found in each of these sentences.
Using all of your powers of observation see if you can find them all.
e.g. In the following sentence we have hidden the word 'corgi':
Although Mike had changed the de<u>cor, G</u>illian still wanted to move house.

1 - At the disco, a charity raffle raised $50 for the youth club.

2 - The falling lid eradicated many of the problems.

3 - At the start rain looked like spoiling everything.

4 - It was either Neil or Ryan who suggested we went for a walk.

5 - It was so cold we had to put rucksacks against the tent door.

42

ADD—A—LETTER

Add the letter 'C' to all these words to make eight brand new ones.
You can put it at the beginning of the word, at the end, or even in the middle.

SENT	RUMBLE
OVER	PLAID
SANDAL	MANIA
MEDIAL	LOCK

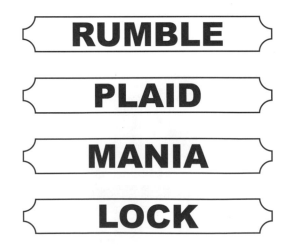

CODEBREAKER

Every letter of the alphabet has been replaced with a number. Your job is to work out which number represents each letter and write it in the grid. We have entered the word TEAK so you know that 13 = T, 17 = E, 24 = A, and 6 = K.
If you get stuck there are two extra letters at the bottom of the page.

Left column: A B C D E F G H I J K L M

Right column: N O P Q R S T U V W X Y Z

Main grid (rows):

9	14	2	17	■	8		8	■	13	14	14	6
14	■	■	26	17	24	13	10	17	2	■	■	19
24	■	■	17	■	7	■	24	■	19	■	■	25
13	23	24	2	■	14	■	18	■	14	3	17	18
■	1	■	■	■	25	11	12	■	■	3	■	■
5	11	20	20	25	17	■	17	23	8	24	5	17
■	24	■	■	14	■	■	■	24	■	■	14	■
5	25	17	18	13	4	■	22	4	5	24	23	23
■	14	■	■	■	14	16	17	■	■	17	■	■
15	2	17	13 (T)	■	18	■	13	■	2	19	16	23
14	■	■	17 (E)	■	16	■	2	■	17	■	■	10
19	■	■	24 (A)	21	17	2	24	12	17	■	■	11
25	11	2	6 (K)	■	2	■	4	■	15	17	24	13

Key grid:

1	2	3	4	5	6	7	8	9	10	11	12	13
					K							T

14	15	16	17	18	19	20	21	22	23	24	25	26
			E							A		

2 = R   8 = C

STEP BY STEP

44

By changing one letter each step, turn YEAR to BOOT in three moves.

YEAR				BOOT
	Grizzly, eg	Regular throb	Gravy jug	

45

OPPOSITES ATTRACT

Match the four words on the left with a word of opposite meaning on the right.

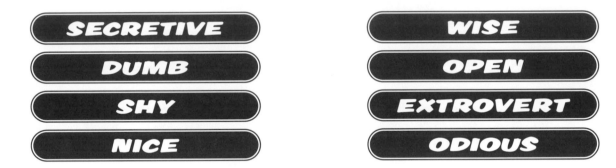

SECRETIVE — WISE
DUMB — OPEN
SHY — EXTROVERT
NICE — ODIOUS

46

INSIDE OUT

We have taken a four-letter word out of each of the words listed below. Can you work out which word should go back 'inside' and make a complete word again?
e.g. OVER should go back inside the letters PR - - - - BS to make PROVERBS.

PA - - - - ET   SE - - - - ED   CR - - - - OR

TO - - - - OR   RE - - - - LY   RE - - - - NT

ARCH • CENT • EDIT • RAKE • READ • SIDE

MISSING LETTERS

One of each letter of the alphabet has been taken from this crossword grid.
Can you put them all back into their correct positions?

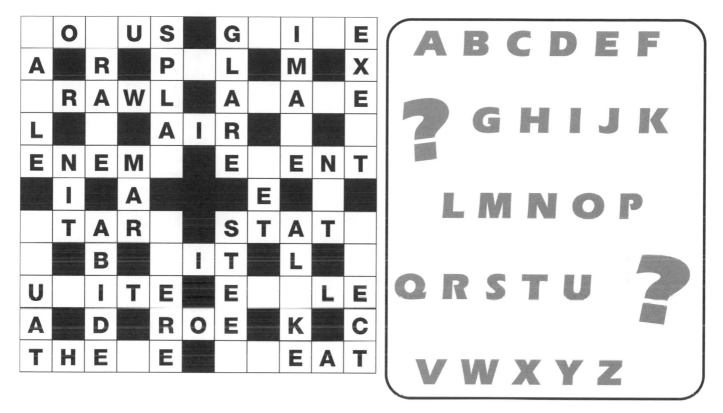

IN A STEW!

Find four creatures by rearranging the letters in each box.

1	2	3	4
L A M E C	O R G A N A K O	P D I N O L H	O I G E P N

LEVEL 1

1: ODD ONE OUT
Oval A = 2
It is the only even number.
Oval B = 15
It is the only odd number.

2: WATCH OUT
Answer = C
The time increases by 1 hour and 5 minutes each step.

3: PYRAMID POSER
Answer = 12
Add the bottom two numbers together to get the top number.
3 + 7 = 10
6 + 3 = 9
8 + 4 = 12

4: ALL SQUARE
Add the three outer numbers and write the answer in the inner corner.

5: DOTTY DOMINOES
Answer = D
The dots on the dominoes in the last column equal the total of all the other dots in the same row.

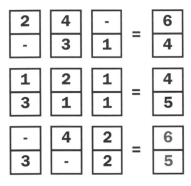

6: CROSS OVER
The middle number in each case is made up of the outer numbers, so that:
A = 2   4 + 7 + 1 + 2 = 14
B = 2   5 + 1 + 3 + 2 = 11
C = 6   1 + 8 + 2 + 6 = 17

7: TRI—PIE
Answer = 18
Moving clockwise around each circle, starting with the lowest number, the numbers increase by 1, then 2, then 3 etc.

8: NUMBER BOX
Answer = 1
Add together the first and second numbers in each line to get the third.
3 + 4 = 7
2 + 1 = 3
5 + 5 = 10

9: WEB WORLD
Answer = 5
The numbers in the inner ring have been moved one place clockwise from the numbers in the outer ring.

10: MAGIC SQUARE
Answer = 15
The four numbers at the corners of the square when added together = 15, and the four numbers that make up the diamond when added together = 15.

11: ALL STAR
Answer = 5
In each star the top number will divide into the other numbers.

12: CIRCLES
Answer = 9
Add together the numbers on the end of each line to get the middle number.

13: BOXING CLEVER
Answer = 17
Double each number and subtract 1 to get the next.

14: MISSING NUMBERS
Answer = 9 and 9
The numbers in each of the segments in the bottom circles are equal to the sum of the corresponding segments in the connected circles above.
Left and center circles:
2 + 7 = 9
4 + 1 = 5
3 + 2 = 5
1 + 5 = 6

Center and right circles:
7 + 2 = 9
1 + 3 = 4
2 + 4 = 6
5 + 4 = 9

15: HONEYCOMB
Answer = 22
All the other numbers are odd.

16: HOLE NUMBERS
Answer = 37
Starting in the top left corner and moving clockwise in a spiral pattern toward the center, add 1, then 2, then 3 etc.

17: FIGURE–IT–OUT
Answer = 989
Add the two outer numbers to get the middle number.

18: SHAPE UP
Answer = 2
Add together each pair of opposite numbers to get the same total.

19: TAKE AWAY
Answer = 3734
Put the two digits from the right hand side in the middle of the two digits from the left hand side.

20: DOTTY
Answer = 6
Add together the numbers on the left-hand side of the shaded column, then add together the numbers on the right and the difference is shown in the center.

21: ROGUE NUMBERS
A = 11   The only odd number
B = 13   The only odd number
C = 12   The only even number
D = 16   The only even number

22: MISSING LINK
Answer = 38
Moving from left to right, add 2, then 3, then 4 etc.

LEVEL 1

23: LINE UP
Line B = 13
Line C = 5
Line D = 6
Line E = 9
Line F = 8
Moving along the rows, add three and then subtract 1, and continue this sequence until the end.

24: CHANGE IT
Answer = 18
The number in the center is mid-way between the outer two numbers in each segment.

25: OPTIONS
Answer = 15
Moving down the first column, up the second and down the third, add three each step.

26: NUMBER SQUARE
Numbers in each row add up to 18.

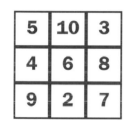

27: STAR STRUCK
Answer = 12
Add up the outer numbers and divide the answer by 2 to get the middle number.

28: TRIO
Answer = 48
Multiply the top two numbers and double it to get the bottom number.

29: GRID LOCK
Answer: A = 1 and B = 8
Taking each box individually, the sum of the digits in each column are the same in each box.

30: LINES OF THOUGHT
Line B = 12
Line C = 10
Line D = 8
Line E = 4
Line F = 24
As you move from left to right, add 2 to the first number, then 3, then 4 etc.

31: PYRAMID POINTERS
Answer = 5
In each triangle, add the lower two numbers together to give the number at the top of the triangle.

32: TIME OUT
Answer = C
Start with the watch on the left and move to the right. The time on each watch increases by 1 hour and 10 minutes each time.

33: STAR STRUCK
Answer = 12
Start with the number at the top of each star, and move clockwise around the star's points. The numbers increase by this top number each time, as you go round.

34: FIGURE—IT—OUT
Answer = 8
In each row and column, add together the left and right hand numbers, or the top and bottom numbers, to get the result in the center of the row or column.

35: SLICED UP
Answer = 16
One way of doing this is to divide each circle in half, vertically. In each half, multiply the top number by the middle number to give the lower number.

36: DOTTY DOMINOES
Answer = A
Start at the top left, and work in rows, from left to right, top to bottom. The spot total on each domino follows the sequence 1, 2, 3, 4...etc.

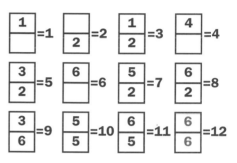

37: CIRCLES
Answer = 9
Work through the diagram in rows. Add the left-hand number to the central number, to get the result in the right-hand circle.

38: DIGITAL DISCS
Answer = 51
Multiply the top two numbers and write the answer, in reverse, in the bottom segment.

39: BOXING CLEVER
Answer = 9
Read each row as a 3-digit number. Starting at the top and working down, numbers are written in sequence, starting at 100, then 121, 144 and 169. These numbers represent the square numbers of 10, 11, 12 and 13.

40: FOUR SQUARE
Answer = 1
There are 2 groups of 4 circles in the diagram, each one defining a square. The sum of the numbers in each square is 14.

41: OUT OF PLACE
Answer = 10
All the other numbers are multiples of 3.

LEVEL 1

42: ET CETERA
Answer = 128
Numbers double each step.

43: NUMBER WHEEL
Answer = 1
Add up the 2 numbers in each segment, and add this total to the sum of the numbers in the opposite segment. This always makes 10.

44: SEQUENTIAL
Answer = 32
As you move from left to right, double the previous number to get the next one along.

45: HOLE IN ONE
Answer = 20
Start with the 4 in the top left of the square, and move in a clockwise spiral toward the center. The numbers follow the sequence of multiples of 4, from 4 to 36.

46: MAGIC SQUARE

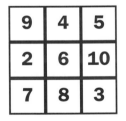

9	4	5
2	6	10
7	8	3

47: MISFITS
A = 21   all numbers are multiples of 5
B = 41   all numbers are multiples of 6
C = 10   all numbers are multiples of 3
D = 15   all numbers are multiples of 4

48: FULL HOUSE
Answer = 16
The number on the roof of each house equals the sum of the numbers in the windows and doors.

49: OPTIONAL EXTRAS
Answer = 12
In each column, add the top number to the middle number to give the result on the bottom row.

50: NUMBER SQUARE
If you add up the 3 numbers in each outer square, the total is always 10.

51: MINDBENDER
$20 profit, on each deal he made a $10 profit.

52: SQUARE DEAL
Answer = 0
Read the 2 separate digits in each box as a whole 2 digit number. Moving from left to right, top row then bottom, the 2 digit numbers increase by 5 each time, from 25 to 40.

53: GONE MISSING
Answer = 3
In each row, add up the numbers to the left of the center, and subtract the numbers to the right of the center, putting the result in the dark circle in the center.

54: NETWORK
Answer A = 1 and B = 5
Add the top number to the bottom number of every column to get the same answer for each grid.

55: WHEEL SPIN
Answer = 7
Add together numbers in matching segments of the upper left and middle circles, putting the results in the segments of the lower left circle. Repeat the same process for the middle and upper right circles.

56: SPACE ODDITY
Oval A = 6
All the numbers are odd.
Oval B = 7
All the numbers are even.

57: RING THE CHANGES
Answer = 5
In each row of the diagram, subtract the right-hand number from the left hand number to give the result in the middle ring.

58: WHACKY WEB
Answer = 4
Add together pairs of numbers, one from an outer segment and one from the inner segment directly opposite. Their total should always be 10.

LEVEL 2

1: ODD ONE OUT
Oval A = 10
It is the only number not divisible by 3.
Oval B = 25
It is the only number not divisible by 7.

2: WATCH OUT
Answer = B
The time decreases by 1 hour and 12 minutes each step.

3: PYRAMID POSER
Answer = 14
Multiply the bottom two numbers together to get the top number.
4 x 5 = 20
3 x 6 = 18
2 x 7 = 14

4: ALL SQUARE
The outer numbers are all divisible by the inner number.

5: DOTTY DOMINOES
Answer = A
The total number of dots on each domino increases by 2 each step of the line.

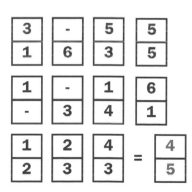

6: CROSS OVER
Add together the numbers at each end of the diagonal lines to get the middle number.
A = 13   7 + 6 = 13 9 + 4 = 13
B = 9   2 + 9 = 11 6 + 5 = 11
C = 2   1 + 7 = 8   2 + 6 = 8

7: TRI—PIE
Answer = 7
Add together the matching segments from the two circles on the right and transfer the answer to the corresponding segment in the third circle.

8: NUMBER BOX
Answer = 6
Multiply together the first and second numbers in each line to get the third.
2 x 3 = 6
3 x 1 = 3
6 x 3 = 18

9: WEB WORLD
Answer = 3
The numbers in the inner ring have been moved one place clockwise from the numbers in the outer ring with 1 subtracted.

10: MAGIC SQUARE
Answer = 3
The four numbers at the corners of the square when added together = 23, and the four numbers that make up the diamond when added together also = 23.

11: ALL STAR
Answer = 12
Starting with the top number and moving clockwise add 1 to get the next number, then 2, then 3 etc.

12: CIRCLES
Answer = 7
Add together the numbers on the end of each line and subtract 2 to get the middle number.

13: BOXING CLEVER
Answer = 82
Multiply each number by 3 and subtract 2 to get the next.

14: MISSING NUMBERS
Answer = 7 and 7
The numbers in each of the segments in the bottom circles are equal to the sum of the corresponding segments in the connected circles above.
Left and center circles:
1 + 7 = 8
5 + 3 = 8
4 + 2 = 6
6 + 1 = 7

Center and right circles:
7 + 1 = 8
3 + 4 = 7
2 + 5 = 7
1 + 3 = 4

15: HONEYCOMB
Answer = 23
All the other numbers are even.

16: HOLE NUMBERS
Answer = 55
Starting in the top left corner and moving clockwise in a spiral pattern toward the center, add together the previous two numbers to get the next.

17: FIGURE IT OUT
Answer = 180
Subtract the number in the third column from the number in the first to get the figure in the middle.

18: SHAPE UP
Answer = 3
Multiply each pair of opposite numbers in each box to get the same answer.

19: TAKE AWAY
Answer = 2678
Taking all four digits in the first and last ovals, write them down in numerical order in the middle.

20: DOTTY
Answer = 9
Add together the numbers on each line and write the answer in the middle column.

LEVEL 2

21: ROGUE NUMBERS
A = 14   All the rest are multiples of 3

B = 14   All the rest are multiples of 4

C = 16   All the rest are multiples of 6

D = 22   All the rest are multiples of 7

22: MISSING LINK
Answer = 59

Moving from left to right, add an extra 2 each step.

23: LINE UP
Line B = 12

Line C = 16

Line D = 28

Line E = 18

Line F = 12

Moving along the row, multiply by 2 then subtract 2 and continue this sequence.

24: CHANGE IT
Answer = 3

Multiply the outer 2 numbers to get the third.

25: OPTIONS
Answer = 12

Moving down the first column, up the second and down the third, add 3 and then 2 alternately each step.

26: NUMBER SQUARE
Numbers in each row add up to 34.

13	3	2	16
8	10	11	5
12	6	7	9
1	15	14	4

27: STAR STRUCK
Answer = 6

Add up the outer numbers and divide it by 3 to get the middle numbers.

28: TRIO
Answer = 15

Multiply the top 2 numbers and divide it by 2 to get the bottom number.

29: GRID LOCK
Answer: A = 6 and B = 4

Taking each box individually, the bottom number is 2 less than the top in grid A and 4 less in grid B.

30: LINES OF THOUGHT
Line B = 1

Line C = 4

Line D = 13

Line E = 9

Line F = 6

In each row, add the first 2 numbers together and add 2 to give the next number along.

31: PYRAMID POINTERS
Answer = 6

In each triangle, add together the bottom 2 numbers and subtract 2 to give the value at the top of the triangle.

32: TIME OUT
Answer = A

Starting with the watch on the left and moving to the right, the time on each watch increases by 50 minutes.

33: STAR STRUCK
Answer = 7

In each star, start at the top point and move clockwise. Add the first 2 numbers together to give the next one along. Continue this pattern all the way around each star.

34: FIGURE IT OUT
Answer = 2

The numbers create a magic square, in which the numbers along any vertical, horizontal, or diagonal line add up to 15.

35: SLICED UP
Answer = 8

Add together numbers in matching segments of the upper left and right-hand circles, and put the result in the matching segments of the lower circle.

36: DOTTY DOMINOES
Answer = C

In each row, starting on the left and moving to the right, the spot total on each domino increases by 2 each time.

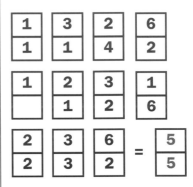

37: CIRCLES
Answer = 8

Work through the diagram in columns. If you multiply the top number by the middle number you get the result, shown by the bottom number.

38: DIGITAL DISCS
Answer = 37

In each circle, multiply the left- and right hand numbers together and subtract 3 to give the lower number.

39: BOXING CLEVER
Answer = 279

In each row of the diagram, add the number in the left-hand column to the number in the right-hand column and put the result in the central column.

LEVEL 2

40: FOUR SQUARE

Answer = 9

Look at the diagram as 2 interlocked squares. Starting with the lowest number in each square, move clockwise around the other numbers. One square contains the sequence of multiples of 2 (2, 4, 6, 8) and the other square contains multiples of 3 (3, 6, 9, 12).

41: OUT OF PLACE

Answer = 44

All the other numbers in the row are square numbers.

42: ET CETERA

Answer = 88

Start on the left and move to the right. Add the first 2 numbers together and add a further 1 to give the next number along.

43: NUMBER WHEEL

Answer = 5

In each segment, add the outer 2 numbers together, then add a further 1 to give the result at the center of the segment.

44: SEQUENTIAL

Answer = 11

As you move from left to right, the numbers follow the sequence of prime numbers.

45: HOLE IN ONE

Answer = 55

Start at the top left of the diagram, and move to the right. Then move down one row and move to the left. Finally, move down one row and to the right, making a snakes and ladders pattern. Add together the first 2 numbers to get the next one along. Repeat this formula while you move around the diagram.

46: MAGIC SQUARE

1	12	8	13
15	6	10	3
14	7	11	2
4	9	5	16

47: MISFITS

A = 71   All the numbers contain a 4
B = 34   All the numbers contain a 7
C = 26   All the numbers contain a 3
D = 19   All the numbers contain a 2

48: FULL HOUSE

Answer = 42

In each house, add up the numbers around the windows and roof of the house and double the result, putting this number in the doorway.

49: OPTIONAL EXTRAS

Answer = 46

Move down the left-hand column, then up the middle, and down the right hand column. Start by adding 2 to the first number, then add 3, 4, 5 etc. all the way around.

50: NUMBER SQUARE

Add together the 3 numbers in each dark shaded square, and then add the number in the lighter shaded square which is closest to the other 3. Their total will always be 15.

51: MINDBENDER

Jack is 52 and Martha is 39.

52: SQUARE DEAL

Answer = 2

Start with the top left-hand square and move clockwise around the others. The sum of the numbers in each square increases by 5 each time, from 10 to 25.

53: GONE MISSING

Answer = 10

In each row, total up the left- and right-hand numbers and divide this total by 2 to give the value in the central line.

54: NETWORK

Answer: A = 35 and B = 56

Starting at the top left of each grid and moving to the right, top row then bottom row, numbers follow multiples of 6 for the left-hand grid, 7 for the middle grid and 8 for the right-hand grid.

55: WHEEL SPIN

Answer = 2   0
         21   9

Multiply the numbers in matching segments of the top left and top center circles to get the numbers shown in the bottom left circle. Repeat this for the top right and top center circles to find the missing numbers.

56: SPACE ODDITY

Oval A = 55
All numbers are multiples of 8
Oval B = 41
All numbers are multiples of 9

57: RING THE CHANGES

Answer = 18

Add together the 2 digits shown in the left- and right-hand ovals and multiply these answers together to get the number in the central oval.

58: WHACKY WEB

Answer = 7

Start with a number from an outer segment of the web, and add it to the number in the inner segment one place clockwise from the original. This sum is always 10.

LEVEL 3

1: ODD ONE OUT
Oval A = 26
It is the only number not containing a 1.
Oval B = 30
It is the only number not containing a 2.

2: WATCH OUT
Answer = D
Digits move one place to the left each step.

3: PYRAMID POSER
Answer = 24
Multiply the bottom 2 numbers and double it to get the top number.

4: ALL SQUARE
Add the 3 outer numbers together and divide by 3 to get the inner number.

5: DOTTY DOMINOES
Answer = C
Moving along the rows, the dots on all 4 dominoes add up to 18.

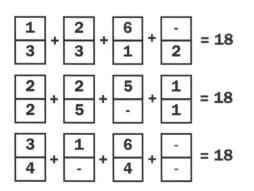

6: CROSS OVER
The middle number in each case is the difference between the numbers on either end of the diagonal lines:
A = 2
B = 3
C = 1

7: TRI—PIE
Answer = 4
The difference between the matching segments from the two circles on the right is written in the corresponding segment in the third circle.

8: NUMBER BOX
Answer = 6
Multiply the first and third numbers in each row and column to get the number in the middle box.

9: WEB WORLD
Answer = 8
Each pair of numbers equals 10.

10: MAGIC SQUARE
Answer = 6
The 4 numbers at the corners of the square when added together equal 20, and the 4 numbers which make up the diamond when added together also equal 20.

11: ALL STAR
Answer = 16
Starting with the top number and moving clockwise, add 2 to get the next number, then subtract 1, add 2, and then finally subtract 1 again.

12: CIRCLES
Answer = 4
Each line of 3 numbers going through the center circle adds up to 12.

13: BOXING CLEVER
Answer = 19
Multiply each number by 2 and then subtract 3 to get the next number.

14: MISSING NUMBERS
Answer = 6 and 6
The numbers in each of the segments in the bottom circles are equal to double the numbers in the matching segments of the connected circles above.

Left and center circles:
7 + 4 = 11 (22)
2 + 1 = 3 (6)
2 + 1 = 3 (6)
3 + 2 = 5 (10)

Center and right circles:
4 + 2 = 6 (12)
3 + 1 = 4 (8)
1 + 4 = 5 (10)
2 + 1 = 3 (6)

15: HONEYCOMB
Answer = 20
All the other numbers are multiples of 3.

16: HOLE NUMBERS
Answer = 7
Starting in the top left corner and moving clockwise in a spiral pattern toward the center, add 2 for the next number, subtract 1 for the next, add 2, subtract 1 etc.

17: FIGURE—IT—OUT
Answer = 1109
Add together the numbers in the first and third columns to get the number in the middle.

18: SHAPE UP
Answer = 5
The sum of the numbers in each square is 24.

19: TAKE AWAY
Answer = 9852
Take all 4 digits shown in each line and write them in reverse numerical order in the middle.

20: DOTTY
Answer = 7
Add together the numbers in each row and divide it by 2 to get the middle number.

21: ROGUE NUMBERS
A = 86, B = 42, C = 130, D = 110
All the others are square numbers. (2x2 = 4, 3x3 = 6, 4x4 = 16 etc.)

LEVEL 3

22: MISSING LINK
Answer = 10
Moving from left to right, add 2 for the next number, then subtract 1 for the next, and continue this sequence.

23: LINE UP
Line B = 4
Line C = 6
Line D = 4
Line E = 0
Line F = 8
Moving along the rows, subtract 1, add 2, subtract 3, add 4, and then subtract 5.

24: CHANGE IT
Answer = 4
Add together the 2 outer numbers in each segment and add 1 to get the number in the middle.

25: OPTIONS
Answer = 9
Moving down the first column, up the second, and down the third, add 4 and then subtract 2 alternately each step.

26: NUMBER SQUARE
Numbers in each row add up to 34.

7	2	9	16
13	12	3	6
4	5	14	11
10	15	8	1

27: STAR STRUCK
Answer = 10
Add up the outer numbers, divide by 2 and then add 3 to get the middle numbers.

28: TRIO
Answer = 41
Multiply the top 2 numbers and write the answer in reverse at the bottom.

29: GRID LOCK
Answer: A = 9 and B = 25
Square the top numbers in each box to get the bottom number.
(3x3 = 9, 5x5 = 25)

30: LINES OF THOUGHT
Line B = 11
Line C = 7
Line D = 13
Line E = 10
Line F = 5
Starting on the left and working to the right, alternately add 4 to the first number, then subtract 1.

31: PYRAMID POINTERS
Answer = 82
Add the bottom 2 numbers and write your answer, in reverse order, at the top of the triangle.

32: TIME OUT
Answer = D
Starting with the watch on the left and moving to the right, the time on each watch increases by 1 hour and 45 minutes.

33: STAR STRUCK
Answer = 5
In each star, add together the top 3 numbers to get a 2 digit answer, and use the bottom 2 points of the star to display the 2 digits.

34: FIGURE IT OUT
Answer = 9
If you add up the numbers in any row or column, their total is always 20.

35: SLICED UP
Answer = 7
Multiply together numbers from matching segments of the upper left- and right-hand circles and put the results in matching segments of the lower circle.

36: DOTTY DOMINOES
Answer = E
The sum of the spots in each column of dominoes is always 16.

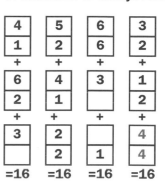

37: CIRCLES
Answer = 97
Start on the top left, and move clockwise in a spiral toward the center. Add the first 2 numbers together to give the next one along. Continue around the rest of the diagram.

38: DIGITAL DISCS
Answer = 8
In each circle, multiply the left- and right-hand numbers together and add the lower number. The result is always 50.

39: BOXING CLEVER
Answer = 6311
Work through the diagram in columns, top to bottom. In the left-hand column, add 1,100 to each number as you go down. For the central column, add 1,400, and for the right-hand column, add 1,700.

40: FOUR SQUARE
Answer = 34
The numbers shown on each point of the diamond are midway between the numbers shown on each point of the square.

41: OUT OF PLACE
Answer = 15
All other numbers in the row are the cube numbers of 1, 2, 3, and 4.

LEVEL 3

42: ET CETERA

Answer = 19
Working from left to right, the numbers represent the sequence of Prime Numbers.

43: NUMBER WHEEL

Answer = 2
In each segment of the circle, add the two outer numbers together and subtract the inner number. The result is always 7.

44: SEQUENTIAL

Answer = 63
As you move from left to right, double each number and add 1 to give the next number along.

45: HOLE IN ONE

Answer = 13
Start at the top left of the diagram and move along the row to the right, then down one row and to the left etc. in a snakes and ladders pattern. Numbers alternately increase by 3 and then decrease by 1.

46: MAGIC SQUARE

10	4	13	7
15	5	12	2
8	14	3	9
1	11	6	16

47: MISFITS

A = 26, B = 26, C = 12, D = 88
All other numbers are multiples of 4 in Box A, 6 in Box B, 8 in Box C, and 13 in Box D.

48: FULL HOUSE

Answer = 10
Add together the four numbers representing the windows and subtract the number representing the door to get the number shown in the roof.

49: OPTIONAL EXTRAS

Answer = 99
Start at the top of the left-hand column, and move down, then to the top of the next column on the right and move down etc. Numbers increase by 5, 7, 9, 11 etc all the way round.

50: NUMBER SQUARE

Add together the 3 digits in each dark gray square, and put this sum in the corner of the light gray square 1/4 turn clockwise from the original square.

51: MINDBENDER

Answer= 10 people
Each one shakes hands with 9 other people (90 shakes) with each handshake shared between 2 people (90 ÷ 2 = 45 shakes).

52: SQUARE DEAL

Answer = 8
In each box, the product of the upper and lower numbers equals the product of the left- and right-hand numbers.

53: GONE MISSING

Answer = 6
If you add up all the numbers in a row then, from top to bottom, the sums make the sequence 5, 10, 15, 20, 25.

54: NETWORK

Answer A = 18 and B = 24
In each grid, multiply the top leftnumber by 2 to give the lower left number; multiply the top middle number by 3 to give the lower middle number and multiply the top right number by 4 to give the lower right number.

55: WHEEL SPIN

Answer =14   6
        10   2
Start with the top left circle, and move in a W shape around the others, following the black line. Multiply the numbers in the first circle by 2 and write the results in matching segments of the next circle along. Then subtract 2 from each of these numbers and write the results in matching segments of the next circle. Repeat this pattern, multiplying the numbers by 2, then subtracting 2.

56: SPACE ODDITY

Oval A = 119
All numbers contain the digit 3.
Oval B = 132
All numbers contain 1 digit that is repeated.

57: RING THE CHANGES

Answer = 5
In each row of the diagram, if you subtract the sum of the left- and right-hand numbers from the central number, the result is always 10.

58: WHACKY WEB

Answer = 22
Start with the central left segment (containing the 3s) and move clockwise around the diagram. The sum of the numbers in the outer and inner segments follow the sequence of multiples of 6, from 6 to 48.

LEVEL 4

1: ODD ONE OUT

Oval A = 35
It is the only number not divisible by 9.
Oval B = 26
It is the only number not divisible by 12.

2: WATCH OUT

Answer = A
The digits shown on each watch add up to 10 every time.

3: PYRAMID POSER

Answer = 20
Multiply the bottom two numbers together and divide it by 2 to get the top number.
3 x 12 = 36 (18)
4 x 7 = 28 (14)
5 x 8 = 40 (20)

4: ALL SQUARE

Multiply the three outer numbers together to get the number in the middle.

5: DOTTY DOMINOES

Answer = D
Moving along the lines, add the dots of the first two dominoes together and then subtract the dots from the third to get the answer shown in the last column.

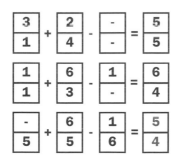

6: CROSS OVER

Multiply the numbers at each end of the diagonal lines to get the middle number.
A = 6
B = 9
C = 18

7: TRI—PIE

Answer = 6
Multiply the matching segments from the two circles on the right and transfer the answer to the corresponding segment in the third circle.

8: NUMBER BOX

Answer = 14
Multiply together the first and second numbers in each line and then divide it by 2 to get the number in the third box.

9: WEB WORLD

Answer = 2
The numbers in the inner ring match those of the outer ring in the opposite segment.

10: MAGIC SQUARE

Answer = 1
The four numbers at the corners of the square when multiplied together = 24, and the four numbers that make up the diamond when multiplied together = 24.

11: ALL STAR

Answer = 5
Starting with the top number and moving clockwise, double each number and subtract 1 to get the next.

12: CIRCLES

Answer = 19
The middle number is midway between the other 2 numbers on each line.

13: BOXING CLEVER

Answer = 106
Add 3 to each number and double it to get the next.

14: MISSING NUMBERS

Answer = 9 and 9
The numbers in each of the segments in the bottom circles are equal to the sum, minus 1, of the corresponding segments in the connected circles above.
Left and center circles:
7 + 3 - 1 = 9
2 + 2 - 1 = 3
3 + 8 - 1 = 10
9 + 1 - 1 = 9

Center and right circles:
3 + 4 - 1 = 6
2 + 9 - 1 = 10
8 + 2 - 1 = 9
1 + 6 - 1 = 6

15: HONEYCOMB

Answer = 34
All the other numbers are multiples of 8.

16: HOLE NUMBERS

Answer = 8
Starting in the top left corner and moving clockwise in a spiral pattern toward the center, add 3 for the next number, subtract 2, and continue this sequence.

17: FIGURE IT OUT

Answer = 2594
The 3 numbers in each row add up to 10,000.

18: SHAPE UP

Answer = 4
Add together the top and bottom numbers. Subtract the right-hand number from the left. The answer is always the same.

19: TAKE AWAY

Answer = 8131
Reverse the digits shown in the small ovals (left then right) and write the figure in the middle.

LEVEL 4

20: DOTTY
Answer = 7
Taking the number shown on each side as a whole number, subtract the right-hand side from the left-hand side.
(701 - 694 = 9)

21: ROGUE NUMBERS
A = 20, B = 33, C = 15, D = 39
All the rest are prime numbers. (Numbers that are only divisible by themselves and 1.)

22: MISSING LINK
Answer = 630
Moving from left to right, multiply by 5 for the next number, subtract 4 for the next and continue this sequence.

23: LINE UP
Line A = 3
Line B = 4
Line C = 36
Line D = 5
Line E = 11
Moving along the row, subtract 1, multiply by 2, subtract 3, multiply by 4, and then subtract 5.

24: CHANGE IT
Answer = 4
The numbers in each segment add up to 15.

25: OPTIONS
Answer = 17
Moving down the first column, up the second and down the third, double the first number to get the second, then subtract 5 for the third, and continue this sequence.

26: NUMBER SQUARE
Numbers in each row add up to 65.

5	2	11	22	25
16	18	9	12	10
23	7	13	19	3
20	14	17	8	6
1	24	15	4	21

27: STAR STRUCK
Answer = 36
Add up the outer numbers and write the answer in reverse in the middle.

28: TRIO
Answer = 71
Multiply the top two numbers, subtract 1 and write the answer in reverse in the bottom segment.

29: GRID LOCK
Answer: A = 14 and B = 11
The numbers in the third boxes in each row and column are the sum of the digits in the first two boxes.

30: LINES OF THOUGHT
Line B = 9
Line C = 19
Line D = 5
Line E = 18
Line F = 4
In each row, there are 2 interlinked sequences. Start with the furthest left-hand octagon, and move to the right, skipping every other octagon, adding 4 each time. Next, start with the second octagon on the left and move to the right, skipping every other octagon, adding 6 each time.

31: PYRAMID POINTERS
Answer = 25
In each pyramid, multiply the bottom left- and right-hand numbers together and add the middle number to give the result at the top.

32: TIME OUT
Answer = C
The times shown on the watches would read the same forward as backward.

33: STAR STRUCK
Answer = 28
In each star, start at the top and move clockwise around the points of the star. In the left-hand star, numbers increase by 1, then 2, then 4 etc. doubling the value each time. Increase the numbers in the middle star by 2, 4, 8 etc. and by 3, 6, 12 etc. in the right-hand star.

34: FIGURE—IT—OUT
Answer = 2
If you add up the numbers in each row of the diagram, the total is always 15.

35: SLICED UP
Answer = 6
Subtract numbers in the right-hand circle from numbers in matching segments of the left-hand circle, putting the results into the lower circle.

36: DOTTY DOMINOES
Answer = D
Work in rows from left to right, top to bottom. Taking consecutive pairs of dominoes, their spot total follows the sequence 5, 6, 7, 8, 9, and 10.

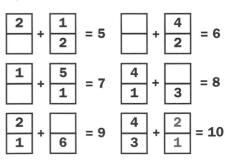

37: CIRCLES
Answer = 28
Start in the top left corner of the diagram and move in a clockwise spiral toward the center. Numbers increase by 3, 4, 5, etc.

LEVEL 4

38: DIGITAL DISCS
Answer = 14
In each circle, double the right- and left-hand numbers, then add them together to give the result in the lower segment.

39: BOXING CLEVER
Answer = 20
Treat each 4- digit number as two 2-digit numbers, side by side. In each row, if you add each pair of numbers together, the answer is always the same—30 for the top row, 35 for the next, then 40, then 45.

40: FOUR SQUARE
Answer = 14
One way of doing this is to start with the 4 on the left and move clockwise. Alternately add 8 to the number, then subtract 3 as you go round.

41: OUT OF PLACE
Answer = 93
All other numbers are multiples of 9.

42: ET CETERA
Answer = 23
Start on the left and move to the right, skipping every other circle, adding 3 each time. Starting with the second circle on the left, and skipping every other circle as before, add 7 each time.

43: NUMBER WHEEL
Answer = 9
Add the outer number of any segment with the inner number from the segment opposite. Their total is always 15.

44: SEQUENTIAL
Answer = 108
As you move to the right, double each number and add 4 to give the next one along.

45: HOLE IN ONE
Answer = 42
Start on the top left of the square and move down. Then right one space and up etc. in a snakes and ladders pattern. Numbers increase alternately by 5, then 4.

46: MAGIC SQUARE

25	10	3	6	21
22	12	19	8	4
11	9	13	17	15
2	18	7	14	24
5	16	23	20	1

47: MISFITS
A = 91, B = 49, C = 95, D = 62
In A and C the second digit in each 2-digit number is 1 higher than the first digit, in B and D they are 1 lower.

48: FULL HOUSE
Answer = 5
In each house, the number in the doorway equals the average of the 5 numbers that surround it.

49: OPTIONAL EXTRAS
Answer = 77
Start at the top left corner and move to the right, then down one row and to the left etc. in a snakes and ladders pattern. Numbers increase by 2, 4, 6, 8, 10 etc.

50: NUMBER SQUARE
In each group of 4 numbers (the 3 bounded by the darker square plus the one from the center light square) the difference between the top 2 numbers is equal to the difference between the lower 2 numbers.

51: MINDBENDER
Answer = 23 years old

52: SQUARE DEAL
Answer = 4
In each square, multiply the top and bottom numbers together, and the left and right numbers together. The sum of these 2 products is always 20.

53: GONE MISSING
Answer = 10
Add together the numbers in the white circles on each row, divide this answer by 2, and subtract 1 to get the number in the black circle.

54: NETWORK
Answer: A = 11 and B = 17
Working in columns, add the top numbers to the bottom numbers, and add 1 to give the central number.

55: WHEEL SPIN
Answer =   2   11
                2   3
Multiply the numbers in matching segments of the top left and top middle circles to get the numbers in the bottom left circle. Repeat this using matching segments of the top right and top middle circles for the bottom right circle.

56: SPACE ODDITY
Oval A = 45
All numbers have a 9 digit in them.
Oval B = 13
All numbers are multiples of 9.

57: RING THE CHANGES
Answer = 14
Working in rows, calculate the difference between the left- and right-hand numbers and double it to give the result in the central oval.

58: WHACKY WEB
Answer = 5
In each slice of the web, multiply the outer segment number by 2 and subtract 3 to give the number in the inner segment.

LEVEL 5

1: ODD ONE OUT
A = 29, B = 116
All other numbers are square numbers.

2: WATCH OUT
Answer = B
The digits shown on the minutes side equal double the total of the digits shown on the hour side.

3: PYRAMID POSER
Answer = 10
Add the bottom digits together to get the top number.
2 + 1 + 3 + 7 = 13
1 + 4 + 2 + 3 = 10
1 + 7 + 2 + 0 = 10

4: ALL SQUARE
Multiply the outer three numbers and divide by 2 to get the inner number.

5: DOTTY DOMINOES
Answer = F
Moving along the lines, the dots on each domino increase by three each step.

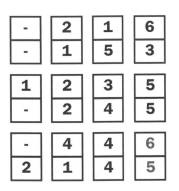

6: CROSS OVER
Multiply the numbers on each end of the diagonal lines and add each answer together to get the middle number.
A = 2, B = 2, C = 31

7: TRI—PIE
Answer = 8
Each pair of opposite numbers equals 10.

8: NUMBER BOX
Answer = 6
Add up the first two numbers in each row and column and then add 1 to get the last number.

9: WEB WORLD
Answer = 5
The numbers in each of the four opposite segments (inner and outer rings) add up to 20.

10: MAGIC SQUARE
Answer = 6
Multiply the four numbers that make up the square to get the same answer you do when multiplying the four numbers that make up the diamond.

11: ALL STAR
Answer = 18
Starting with the top number and moving counterclockwise, double each number and subtract 2 to get the next number.

12: CIRCLES
Answer = 4
Add together the numbers on the end of each line and double it to get the middle number.

13: BOXING CLEVER
Answer = 36
The numbers will be the first five square numbers. (2x2 = 4, 3x3 = 9, 4x4 = 16, 5x5 = 25, and 6x6 = 36)

14: MISSING NUMBERS
Answer = 7 and 7
The numbers in each of the segments in the bottom circles are equal to half the sum of the matching segments in the connected circles above.
Left and center circles:
7 + 9 = 16 (8)
4 + 6 = 10 (5)
2 + 10 = 12 (6)
9 + 7 = 16 (8)

Center and right circles:
9 + 5 = 14 (7)
6 + 6 = 12 (6)
10 + 4 = 14 (7)
7 + 3 = 10 (5)

15: HONEYCOMB
Answer = 54
The digits shown in the other numbers always add up to 10.

16: HOLE NUMBERS
Answer = 14
Starting in the top left corner and moving clockwise in a spiral pattern toward the center, add 9, subtract 8, add 7, subtract 6, etc.

17: FIGURE—IT—OUT
Answer = 8068
Add together the numbers in the first and third columns and write the answer in reverse in the middle column.

18: SHAPE UP
Answer = 5
Multiply the top and bottom numbers and write the answer as single digits on the left and right.

19: TAKE AWAY
Answer = 7647
Taking all four digits shown in the first and last ovals, write this figure down in reverse in the middle.

20: DOTTY
Answer = 9
The figure in the middle column is the same as the highest number in each row.

21: ROGUE NUMBERS
A = 720, B = 864, C = 324, D = 1020
All other numbers are cube numbers. (2x2x2 = 8, 3x3x3 = 27 etc.)

LEVEL 5

22: MISSING LINK

Answer = 165
Moving from left to right, multiply by 5 for the next number, then subtract 7 for the next, and continue this sequence.

23: LINE UP

Line A = 28
Line B = 12
Line C = 8
Line D = 24
Line E = 54
Line F = 73
Moving along the rows, divide by 2, add 4, multiply by 3, add 7, and subtract 3.

24: CHANGE IT

Answer = 4
The total of the numbers in each segment increases by 1 moving clockwise around the circle.

25: OPTIONS

Answer = 22
Moving down the first column, up the second and down the third, double the first number to get the next, subtract 4 for the next and then add 1. Continue this sequence until the end.

26: NUMBER SQUARE

Numbers in each row add up to 65

9	3	22	16	15
2	21	20	14	8
25	19	13	7	1
18	12	6	5	24
11	10	4	23	17

27: STAR STRUCK

Answer = 88
Add up the outer numbers, add 1, and then write the answer in reverse in the middle.

28: TRIO

Answer = 15
Multiply the top two numbers and treble it to get the bottom number.

29: GRID LOCK

Answer: A = 81 and B = 71
The numbers in the third boxes in each row and column are the sum of the digits in the first two boxes in reverse.

30: LINES OF THOUGHT

Line B = 10
Line C = 9
Line D = 20
Line E = 6
Line F = 30
Starting on the left of every row and moving to the right, add 4 to the first number, then 5 to the next. Repeat this sequence, alternately adding 4 then 5.

31: PYRAMID POINTERS

Answer = 30
In each pyramid, multiply the lower two numbers together to give the top number, then halve this to give the number in the center.

32: TIME OUT

Answer = C
Increase all digits by 1 and then move all digits to the left, with the first digit being moved to the far right. For example—210 becomes 321 after adding 1, changing to 213 when the first digit is moved to the far right.

33: STAR STRUCK

Answer = 6
Multiply the numbers shown on the left-hand side, repeat this for the numbers on the right. The top number is the difference between these two answers.

34: FIGURE—IT—OUT

Answer = 15
Working in columns, add the top number to the middle number and divide this total by 2 to give the lower number.

35: SLICED UP

Answer = 18
Start with the number in the top left circle, and add 5 to each one to give the results in matching segments of the lower circle. Next, add 6 to each of the numbers in the lower circle to give the results in matching segments of the top right circle.

36: DOTTY DOMINOES

Answer = A
Working in columns, add the spot total of the upper domino to the lower domino, to give the spot total of the central domino.

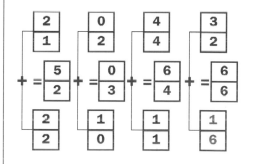

37: CIRCLES

Answer = 49
Start at the top left and move to the right, then down one row and to the left etc. like a snakes and ladders pattern. Add 5 to the first number, then 6, then 7, repeating this sequence as you move around the square.

38: DIGITAL DISCS

Answer = 12
In each circle, multiply the left- and right-hand numbers together and divide the result by 3 to give the lower number.

LEVEL 5

39: BOXING CLEVER

Answer = 6

Work in rows, from top to bottom. If you add up the separate digits in each 4-digit number, you get the same result for each row—in the first row, the total is always 12, for the second it's 13, then 14, then 15 for the bottom row.

40: FOUR SQUARE

Answer = 6

Look at the diagram as 2 intersecting squares, at 45 degrees to each other. The sum of the digits in each square equals 45.

41: OUT OF PLACE

Answer = 36

All other numbers are multiples of 8.

42: ET CETERA

Answer = 44

Start on the left and move to the right. Add the first two numbers together to give the next one, then add 2 to this number to give the one after that. Repeat this sequence all the way along.

CHAPTER 1

1: ADD-A-LETTER
Add the letter T to make the following words.

STILL	THORN
STAND	TOOT
TRIM	FLUTE
PLEAT	TRUE

2: HIDDEN WORDS
You can find the following gemstones hidden among the sentences.
1. Ruby
2. Diamond
3. Opal
4. Topaz
5. Pearl

3: ODD ONE OUT
MELBOURNE.
Because the rest are European.

4: FIRST AND LAST

TALK	KILL
SEVEN	NEW
MINI	ICE
SCARF	FUEL
TILE	EGO

New word = KNIFE

5: CROSSWORD

6: WHEEL SPIN
The letter R replaces the question mark to make the word FATHER.

7: NEXT-IN-LINE
The word EASTER follows on as the first letter, (E), is the next in line alphabetically.

8: LINK WORDS
The link word is LIGHT.

LIGHTHOUSE	HEADLIGHT
LIGHTBULB	LIGHT BRIGADE
SUNLIGHT	DAY LIGHT

9: X-WORDS
SQUARE
OBLONG

10: CODEBREAKER

11: SCRAMBLED
1. ACCIDENT
2. FOOTPATH
3. DISHWASHER
4. JIGSAW PUZZLE
5. BROWNIE
6. PANTOMIME
7. TEACHER
8. SHAMPOO
9. JELLYFISH
10. IMPROVE
11. WHISPER
12. AFTERNOON

12: FIVE STAR
1. A (PANSY)
2. D (DAISY)
3. P (POPPY)

13: ROGUE WORD
CHARMER
The other words all mean the same thing

14: JIG-SAW JUMBLE

F	A	T	E	B	A	S	I	L	
A	B	O	R	I	G	I	N	E	
N	O	M	A	D	E	D	G	E	
S	U	B	M	I	T	E	L	K	
A	T	E	E	N	A	M	E	L	
T	A	X	T	H	R	I	C	E	
A	R	E	N	A	S	N	A	P	
P	E	R	I	L	P	U	R	E	
E	A	T	T	E	A	S	E	R	

15: SCRAMBLE
REACTION

16: TWINS
Words left out are NEVER and TOTAL

1	2
TALLEST	HIGHEST
ANGRY	CROSS
PLEASED	HAPPY
DAMP	MOIST
SMART	CLEVER
LARGE	BIG

17: ALL CHANGE

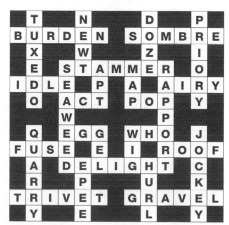

18: VOWEL PLAY

T		N		D		P
BURDEN			SOMBRE			
X		W		Z		I
E	STAMMER					O
IDLE		P	A		AIRY	
O	ACT		POP		Y	
	W			P		
Q	EGG		WHO		J	
FUSE		E	I		ROOF	
A	DELIGHT				C	
R		P		U		K
TRIVET		GRAVEL				
Y		E		L		Y

CHAPTER 1

19: ANAGRAM TIMER
1. CHARM
2. HARM
3. ARM
4. MARE
5. DREAM

20: INCOMPLETE

21: STEP LADDER
LOVE
1. DOVE
2. DOTE
3. DATE
HATE

22: PROVERBS

A MISS is as good as a MILE

Every DOG is allowed one BITE

Great OAKS from little acorns GROW

23: OPPOSITES ATTRACT
OUT	IN
DARK	LIGHT
SWEET	SOUR
FAST	SLOW

24: MIX-UP
1. CARROT
2. CABBAGE
3. SWEDE
4. PARSNIP

25: PICTURE THIS
CARNIVAL

26: QUICK CHANGE

27: CROSSWORD

28: TRIANGLE TWINS
Words left out are AMBITION and MAIN.

1	2
PEEL	FLAKE
BEAST	BRUTE
ABODE	HOME
GLOAT	CROW
COINCIDE	CLASH
CONVENIENT	USEFUL

29: STAR STRUCK
1. F (SWIFT)
2. B (ROBIN)
3. V (RAVEN)

30: ODDITY
LEMONADE.
Because the rest are eaten.

31: DARTBOARD
DART, DRAW, DOOR, & DEAL

32: FIRST & LAST
FISH	HOLD
MILE	EVER
TOLL	LAMP
FILL	LINK
HALO	OLDER

New word = HELLO

33: LINK UP
The link word is ICE.
BLACK ICE	ICE CUBE
DRY ICE	ICE BOX
ICE COLD	ICE CREAM

34: ALL MIXED UP
1. CASUALTY
2. EXAMINED
3. FRAGRANT
4. LINESMAN
5. LINGERIE
6. MARRIAGE
7. SIDEWALK
8. PROGRESS
9. SABOTAGE
10. SMOULDER
11. SURPRISE
12. TRANSFER

35: ABACUS
PINK, RED, GRAY, & BLUE

36: WHAT COMES NEXT?
The word EGYPT follows on as the first letter, E, is the next in line alphabetically.

37: ANAGRAMS
CAUTION

38: BITS 'N' PIECES

E	G	O	C	H	A	I	R	S
R	E	P	A	I	R	D	O	H
A	L	A	R	M	C	L	U	E
A	L	L	A	R	R	E	S	T
S	E	A	T	E	A	F	E	E
H	A	R	A	S	S	O	W	N
A	D	O	R	E	C	R	A	G
R	E	S	I	N	A	C	R	E
T	R	E	A	T	L	E	N	T

CHAPTER 1

39: TIME FOR AN ANAGRAM
1. TRACK
2. TACK
3. CAT
4. FACT
5. CRAFT

40: WHAT, NO VOWELS!

41: HIDDEN WORDS
You can find the following dogs hidden amongst the sentences:
1. Lurcher
2. Jackal
3. Beagle
4. Spaniel
5. Collie

42: ADD-A-LETTER
Add the letter A to make the following words:

ACROSS RAIDER
FORAGE REVEAL
AMUSE TAINT
HOARSE WAIT

43: CODEBREAKER

44: STEP BY STEP
WEST
1. VEST
2. VAST
3. VASE
VALE

45: OPPOSITES ATTRACT
LIGHT   DARK
MINUTE   LARGE
EXCELLENT   BAD
START   TERMINATE

46: INSIDE OUT
FLAMENCO   PATRIOTS
NUTHATCH   CHITCHAT
SCROLLED   APPEARED

47: MISSING LETTERS

48: IN A STEW
1. PARIS
2. BRUSSELS
3. MADRID
4. BERLIN

CHAPTER 2

1: ADD-A-LETTER
Add the letter N to make the following words.

CANTER	SLANT
PANT	SPLINT
NICE	PINE
DUNE	BENT

2: HIDDEN WORDS
You can find the following birds hidden among the sentences.
1. Puffin
2. Eagle
3. Hawk
4. Kite
5. Sparrow

3: ODD ONE OUT
BROWN.
It is the only color from the five listed that is not in the rainbow.

4: FIRST AND LAST

BASIC	CLOT
TUNA	ACE
CLAN	NICE
TOLD	DENT
STALL	LEAD
TALE	ELK

New word = CANDLE

5: CROSSWORD

6: WHEEL SPIN
The letter O replaces the question mark to make the word SCHOOL.

7: NEXT-IN-LINE
The word UNION follows on as the words start with vowels, A, E, I, O, U.

8: LINK WORDS
The link word is CARPET.

CARPET SLIPPERS	CARPET TILES
MAGIC CARPET	RED CARPET
CARPET SWEEPER	CARPET BAG

9: X-WORDS
TWELVE
TWENTY

10: CODEBREAKER

1	2	3	4	5	6	7	8	9	10	11	12	13
X	P	G	U	V	T	Y	Q	E	K	M	I	N

14	15	16	17	18	19	20	21	22	23	24	25	26
J	H	B	F	A	D	W	C	L	O	S	R	Z

11: SCRAMBLED
1. PORRIDGE
2. SHOULDER
3. CAPITAL
4. HISTORY
5. FUNFAIR
6. MAGICIAN
7. BASEBALL
8. UNHAPPY
9. TOURIST
10. NEIGHBOR
11. CANTEEN
12. STATION

12: FIVE STAR
1. G (EAGLE)
2. G (GOOSE)
3. N (FINCH)

13: ROGUE WORD
WASTE
The other words all mean the same thing

14: JIG-SAW JUMBLE

S	E	E	D	Y	A	C	T	S
H	A	L	E	E	R	A	S	E
A	S	S	E	N	T	N	A	N
K	E	E	P	A	B	O	R	T
E	G	G	A	R	R	E	S	T
C	H	R	O	M	E	S	H	E
R	O	A	R	S	W	O	R	N
O	U	T	T	I	E	Y	E	S
P	L	E	A	T	R	A	D	E

15: SCRAMBLE
SILENCED

16: TWINS
Words left out are LIGHT and DARK

1	2
TIRED	SLEEPY
MONEY	CASH
PRETTY	BEAUTIFUL
DIRTY	GRUBBY
SCARE	FRIGHTEN
PUSH	SHOVE

17: ALL CHANGE

T	R	A	C	E
R	I	N	S	E
E	A	G	E	R
D	R	E	A	D
M	E	L	O	N

CHAPTER 2

18: VOWEL PLAY

	A		I		A	
A	S	C	O	U	N	D	R	E	L
Z	I	P	X	J	E		E	W	E
N		E	Q	U	A	L		H	
T	H	E	N	R		Y	E	T	I
R		R		E		Y		R	
F	I	B	U	L	A		M	A	R	B	L	E
	C		P	M			I		W
A	N	T	E		K	E	P	I	N
T			C	O	R	G	I		
T	E	A	H	V	S		A	D	D
	P	R	O	F	E	S	S	O	R
	E		L			L			T

19: ANAGRAM TIMER
1. STRAP
2. STAR
3. RAT
4. TRAP
5. PARTY

20: INCOMPLETE

C	O	U	C	H		O	B	E	S	E
R		S		O	W	N		X		L
E	Q	U	A	L		S	E	I	Z	E
P		A		L	I	E		L		C
T	A	L	L	Y		T	R	E	A	T
	G		O				A		R	
F	E	I	G	N		P	Y	G	M	Y
J		N		O	D	E		U		O
O	V	E	R	T		T	R	A	C	K
R		P		C	U	T		R		E
D	I	T	C	H		Y	O	D	E	L

21: STEP LADDER
GOAT
1. GOAL
2. FOAL
3. FOOL
WOOL

22: PROVERBS

He who PAYS the piper CALLS the tune

One man's MEAT is another man's POISON

Time and TIDE wait for no MAN

23: OPPOSITES ATTRACT
KIND   CRUEL
NAUGHTY   GOOD
DIFFICULT   EASY
UP   DOWN

24: MIX-UP
1. FRANCE
2. KENYA
3. THAILAND
4. BRAZIL

25: PICTURE THIS
DICTATOR

26: QUICK CHANGE

O	R	G	A	N
T	O	R	S	O
T	O	A	S	T
A	D	D	E	R
S	T	E	A	L

27: GROUPS
OBSERVANCE	of	HERMITS
MELODY	of	HARPERS
EXALTATION	of	LARKS
SIEGE	of	CRANES
WATCH	of	NIGHTINGALES
PARLIAMENT	of	OWLS
COLONY	of	RABBITS
TRIP	of	SHEEP
HUSK	of	HARES
TRIBE	of	GOATS
KENNEL	of	RACHES
CRY	of	HOUNDS

28: TRIANGLE TWINS
Words left out are CLUMSY and MAIN.

1	2
SNAG	HITCH
EQUIP	SUPPLY
FORCE	STRENGTH
BIJOU	SMALL
CROSS	ANGRY
GRAVE	SERIOUS

29: STAR STRUCK
1. K (BLACK)
2. R (BROWN)
3. G (GREEN)

30: ODDITY
BUDGIE.
This is the only animal that can fly.

31: DARTBOARD
SNOW, SNUB, SIZE, & SALE.

32: FIRST & LAST
THROW	WONDER
ROTTER	RUNNY
SCAMPI	ICE
GUESS	SWITCH
WHIST	TUNNEL

New word = WRIST

33: LINK UP
The link word is SOAP.

SOAP POWDER	OLD SOAP
SOAP DISH	SOAP BUBBLE
SOAP OPERA	SOAP FLAKE

34: ALL MIXED UP
1. APOLOGIZE
2. BILLIARDS
3. BRIDLEWAY
4. BREAKFAST
5. CASSEROLE
6. COLLECTED
7. EAVESDROP
8. GRADUALLY
9. HURRICANE
10. LETHARGIC
11. ACCURATE
12. BIRTHDAY

CHAPTER 2

35: ABACUS
WREN, ROBIN, JAY, & ROOK.

36: WHAT COMES NEXT?
The word UMPIRE follows on as the words start with vowels, A, E, I, O, U.

37: ANAGRAMS
DISEASE

38: BITS 'N' PIECES

```
O W N R A B B L E
F R A U D A R I A
F O N D D R I F T
A T T E N D N E W
L E E S O B E R A
S L A T R O T O R
L A D R A N O D D
A M O U R G L E E
M E E T C O L O N
```

39: TIME FOR AN ANAGRAM
1. SPILL
2. PILL
3. ILL
4. LILT
5. STILL

40: WHAT, NO VOWELS!

41: HIDDEN WORDS
You can find the following capital cities hidden amongst the sentences:
1. Moscow
2. Lisbon
3. Athens
4. Madrid
5. Paris

42: ADD-A-LETTER
Add the letter T to make the following words:

CHASTE	PLANET
COVERT	TAUNT
DIVERT	STEAL
NATIVE	WEIGHT

43: CODEBREAKER

```
T H I N   D   I   A M E N
O     A C R O N Y M     E
W     P   O   J   I     X
N A M E   W   U   D U C T
  P     S I R     O
A P A T H Y   E N G U L F
  O   U       O     L
V I S A G E   S T A K E S
  N     N I T       G
S T A B   R   A   B L E W
I     O   I   T   A     A
Z   L A C Q U E R       G
E A S T   H   S   B I T E
```

1	2	3	4	5	6	7	8	9	10	11	12	13
H	D	Q	J	S	B	E	I	C	R	X	N	G

14	15	16	17	18	19	20	21	22	23	24	25	26
O	U	T	A	Y	W	V	Z	K	F	P	M	L

44: STEP BY STEP
FOOT
1. FORT
2. PORT
3. PART
PARK

45: OPPOSITES ATTRACT

SHOUT	WHISPER
HAPPY	SAD
INSIDE	EXTERIOR
YOUNG	ANCIENT

46: INSIDE OUT

SECURELY	PLACIDLY
STRATEGY	MERINGUE
INSIGNIA	SPROCKET

47: KEY SEQUENCE
CLEFT
Turn the keys upside down and read the word formed by the lock ends.

48: IN A STEW
1. LEEDS
2. BRADFORD
3. PLYMOUTH
4. NORWICH

CHAPTER 3

1: ADD-A-LETTER
Add the letter R to make the following words:

BIRD   HEARD
CROCK   TRIED
BREAST   STRAND
CRANE   TRIP

2: HIDDEN WORDS
You can find the following colours hidden among the sentences.
1. Green
2. Magenta
3. Pink
4. Black
5. Orange

3: ODD ONE OUT
HORSE.
Because the rest are meat eaters.

4: FIRST AND LAST
HALO   OUT
SLOP   PLAY
PIE   ETCH
CAR   RING
ROTA   AIL
New word = OPERA

5: CROSSWORD

6: WHEEL SPIN
The letter S replaces the question mark to make the word SISTER.

7: NEXT-IN-LINE
The word SPARE follows on as the last letter follows the sequence A,B,C,D,E.

8: LINK WORDS
The link word is MASTER.

MASTER PLAN   PAST MASTER
HEAD MASTER   MASTER KEY
MASTER PIECE   MASTER MIND

9: X-WORDS
CLEVER
BRIGHT

10: CODEBREAKER

11: SCRAMBLED
1. ADVENTURE
2. HAIRDRESSER
3. MISERABLE
4. FRAGILE
5. SNAPSHOT
6. GRANDMA
7. BEHAVE
8. NETBALL
9. SPEARMINT
10. FANCY DRESS
11. BECAUSE
12. WRINKLE

12: FIVE STAR
1. R (GRAPE)
2. P (APPLE)
3. L (MELON)

13: ROGUE WORD
DUST
The other words all mean the same thing

14: JIG-SAW JUMBLE

```
W E A K T R Y S T
A X L E R O U T E
G E L B E A C O N
E R R A N D C O S
S T A B D R A P E
C O N C L U D E D
O P T O A R O D E
P E E R R A N G E
E N D E D L E E R
```

15: SCRAMBLE
RELATION

16: TWINS
Words left out are TENT and PRINT

1	2
HIT	CLOUT
GHOST	SPECTER
FAST	QUICK
TIDY	NEAT
TRY	ATTEMPT
FLOWER	BLOSSOM

17: ALL CHANGE

```
P E D A L
G R A T E
R A N G E
R E C A P
O C E A N
```

CHAPTER 3

18: VOWEL PLAY

```
W A D E   F   O   F I L L
I   O   B U G G Y   N   Y
S Q U I R E   R A I S I N
E   B   E L V E R   U   X
    C L O D   E   D I R T
K E E P     R     T E R M
    L   E R R A T I C   A
S L U R     N     H A S H
    O P A L   D   M Y T H
J   K   A M A Z E   T   M
A V E R S E   A N N E X E
C   E   S O U N D   N   A
K E P T   W   Y   I D O L
```

19: ANAGRAM TIMER
1. TRACK
2. RACK
3. CAR
4. RACE
5. CLEAR

20: INCOMPLETE

```
E X C E L   S M E A R
M   O   O W L   R   E
B A N J O   E Q U I P
E   G   S H E   P   A
D R A K E   T A T T Y
  Y   I       L   A
F E I N T   L E D G E
R   M   R O E   I   N
A M A Z E   V I V I D
M   G   A C E   E   E
E M E N D   L U R I D
```

21: STEP LADDER
FIRE
1. WIRE
2. WORE
3. WORD
WOOD

22: PROVERBS
Don't wash your DIRTY linen in PUBLIC

Many HANDS make light WORK

Many a true WORD spoken in JEST

23: OPPOSITES ATTRACT

PLIABLE	RIGID
UGLY	PRETTY
LEFT	RIGHT
FAT	THIN

24: MIX-UP
1. OCTOBER
2. AUGUST
3. MARCH
4. NOVEMBER

25: PICTURE THIS
GRANDSON

26: QUICK CHANGE

```
R E C A P
N U R S E
S T O N E
P H A S E
B A K E R
```

27: CROSSWORD

28: TRIANGLE TWINS
Words left out are LEAST and CONTENT.

1	2
PIER	QUAY
EXTENT	LIMIT
PERMIT	ALLOW
DARING	BRAVE
SCATTY	DOTTY
SHREWD	CLEVER

29: STAR STRUCK
1. B (BACON)
2. T (STEAK)
3. H (CHOPS)

30: ODDITY
BROTHER.
Because the rest are female relatives.

31: DARTBOARD
GAME, GOAL, GRAB, & GOLD.

32: FIRST & LAST

MEDIC	CURSE
RETAIL	LOVE
PUMA	ACORN
TRUSS	SAVAGE
GRASS	SEASON

New word = CLASS

33: LINK UP
The link word is STICK.

FRENCH STICK	STICK DOWN
WALKING STICK	STICK AROUND
STICK INSECT	STICK UP

34: ALL MIXED UP
1. DEMONSTRATE
2. GREENGROCER
3. HEADQUARTERS
4. INGREDIENTS
5. OCCASIONALLY
6. REPLACEMENT
7. THUNDERBOLT
8. BROOMSTICK
9. DISHWASHER
10. EXTINGUISH
11. JOURNALIST
12. RESTAURANT

CHAPTER 3

35: ABACUS
CAT, DOG, COW, & RAT.

36: WHAT COMES NEXT?
The word CLONE follows on as the last letter follows the sequence A, B, C, D, E.

37: ANAGRAMS
GENERAL

38: BITS 'N' PIECES

39: TIME FOR AN ANAGRAM
1. DREAM
2. REAM
3. ARM
4. RAMP
5. TRAMP

40: WHAT, NO VOWELS!

41: HIDDEN WORDS
You can find the following European countries hidden amongst the sentences:
1. France
2. Spain
3. Portugal
4. Sweden
5. Norway

42: ADD-A-LETTER
Add the letter N to make the following words:

WANDER	SHUNT
RATION	HEAVEN
PRINCE	FRIEND
NEARLY	CINDER

43: CODEBREAKER

44: STEP BY STEP
HEAD
1. LEAD
2. LEND
3. LAND
LANE

45: OPPOSITES ATTRACT

FRESH	STALE
SWEET	RANCID
SPRINT	AMBLE
APPLAUD	JEER

46: INSIDE OUT

PROGRESS	APPARENT
MACHINES	DESPOTIC
DIABETIC	ENTWINED

47: MISSING LETTERS

48: IN A STEW
1. SOCCER
2. SNOOKER
3. CRICKET
4. HOCKEY

CHAPTER 4

1: ADD-A-LETTER
Add the letter P to make the following words:

PLAY
PLIGHT
PATCH
PART
SLOPE
SPLASH
LEAD
PLATE

2: HIDDEN WORDS
You can find the following metals hidden among the sentences.
1. Copper
2. Brass
3. Gold
4. Chrome
5. Tin

3: ODD ONE OUT
NOUGAT.
Because it is the only candy in the list that does not contain an E.

4: FIRST AND LAST
BIB
BAR
SKI
HOLD
LEG
MINE
BEACH
RIND
IRE
DIMPLE
GONE
ELOPE
New word = BRIDGE

5: CROSSWORD

6: WHEEL SPIN
The letter Z replaces the question mark to make the word PUZZLE.

7: NEXT-IN-LINE
The word PASSION follows on as the words increase by one letter each time, 3, 4, 5, 6, and 7.

8: LINK WORDS
The link word is FIELD.
FIELD TRIP
FIELD MOUSE
AIRFIELD
CORNFIELD
FIELD DAY
BATTLE FIELD

9: X-WORDS
COLLIE
POODLE

10: CODEBREAKER

1	2	3	4	5	6	7	8	9	10	11	12	13
A	B	Y	H	P	Z	T	J	S	C	N	X	F

14	15	16	17	18	19	20	21	22	23	24	25	26
E	W	G	R	I	M	O	L	U	V	D	K	Q

11: SCRAMBLED
1. NICKNAME
2. CENTURY
3. MAYONNAISE
4. AIRPORT
5. RUBBISH
6. SPRINTER
7. CURTAIN
8. CARDBOARD
9. ABSENT
10. MISTAKE
11. WONDERFUL
12. SEASHORE

12: FIVE STAR
1. S (SHIRT)
2. R (APRON)
3. K (SOCKS)

13: ROGUE WORD
BRUTE
The other words all mean the same thing.

14: JIG-SAW JUMBLE

```
W A L K  A D E P T
E N E R G Y M A R
E N T I R E B Y E
N U R S E B E A M
E L O P E E R G O
E S T A T E H E R
D O W N A D A P T
L O A D C U R I O
E N D A T E D E N
```

15: SCRAMBLE
TRAINERS

16: TWINS
Words left out are WATER and SAND

1	2
CALM	SERENE
TEAM	GROUP
CANDY	TREATS
PLACE	POSITION
TEST	TRIAL
PULL	YANK

17: ALL CHANGE

```
P E T A L
W R O N G
S K A T E
H A S T E
T U T O R
```

CHAPTER 4

18: VOWEL PLAY

```
S E V E R E   G A L A X Y
E   O   V   O F   E
Q U I T E   W   W A I L
  D E R R I N G E R   L E
  I   N     L
N O N E   S     L O R D
      P E R T U R B
C O M A   A     E M I R
A   T   N     I   A
J   S H O R T H A N D   F
O K A Y   E A   G A F F
L   I   A   Z   T   L
E N D E A R   E N R A G E
```

19: ANAGRAM TIMER
1. PAINT
2. PANT
3. PAT
4. TAPE
5. PETAL

20: INCOMPLETE

```
M I G H T   V O G U E
A   O   W E E   R   V
J U I C E   G L A Z E
O   N   E R A   I   R
R I G I D   N A N N Y
  L   R     P   O
S L E E P   S T U D S
Q   X   A R K   N   I
U N I O N   I N F E R
I   S   S U N   I   E
B I T T Y   T I T A N
```

21: STEP LADDER
BONE
1. BOND
2. BEND
3. BEAD
HEAD

22: PROVERBS
KILL not the goose that lays the GOLDEN egg

A BIRD in the hand is worth two in the BUSH

A rolling STONE gathers no MOSS

23: OPPOSITES ATTRACT
STUPID	CLEVER
OFF	ON
LIGHT	HEAVY
GOOD	BAD

24: MIX-UP
1. JUPITER
2. SATURN
3. MERCURY
4. VENUS

25: PICTURE THIS
MODERATE

26: QUICK CHANGE

```
A M B E R
C A R O L
S H E L F
T R A C E
P A D R E
```

27: CROSSWORD

```
S   B   F I R E W O R K S
T O R E   N   X   M   N
O   E   D E P L E T E D
C H A S T E   L   N   W
K   K   X   O   E   C
P O D G Y   P I M E N T O
I   O   S A T   I   N
L A W S U I T   B E G A N
E   N   B   S   M   E
  C   Y   L   M O S A I C
J U V E N I L E   T   T
  R   A   N   L   R I P E
S E G R E G A T E   C   D
```

28: TRIANGLE TWINS
Words left out are CHIEF and INEPT.

1	2
MIX	BLEND
LOYAL	FAITHFUL
ACRID	PUNGENT
BANISH	EXPEL
RASCAL	KNAVE
HUMOROUS	FUNNY

29: STAR STRUCK
1. M (MOLAR)
2. T (TOOTH)
3. G (FANGS)

30: ODDITY
WASHINGTON.
Because it is the only capital city.

31: DARTBOARD
CHIN, CITY, CONE & CLAP.

32: FIRST & LAST
STREAM MOUSE

BRAVO	OVEN
SWORN	NEVER
TRAIT	TIGHT
WINCH	HAND

New word = MONTH

33: LINK UP
The link word is POCKET.

POCKET MONEY	CORNER POCKET
PICK POCKET	HIP POCKET
POCKET KNIFE	AIR POCKET

34: ALL MIXED UP
1. SPEARHEAD
2. SUPERSTAR
3. TOOTHACHE
4. VEGETABLE
5. ACCELERATE
6. CONVENIENT
7. EMBROIDERY
8. INSTRUCTOR
9. NATIONWIDE
10. SKYSCRAPER
11. VEGETARIAN
12. UNEMPLOYED

35: ABACUS
TULIP, ROSE LILY, & PANSY.

36: WHAT COMES NEXT?
The word MELLOW follows on as the second letter follows the alphabetical sequence, A, B, C, D, and E.

37: ANAGRAMS
FUNFAIR

38: BITS 'N' PIECES

```
L A P D E L E T E
E R A E X I L E D
S C R A P E S A G
S C O N E D E F Y
C O P O L D S E A
R O T A D E T E R
A D D S A F A R I
V I A I R E G A S
E N D S E R E N E
```

39: TIME FOR AN ANAGRAM
1. STILE
2. LIST
3. LIT
4. TILE
5. LITHE

40: WHAT, NO VOWELS!

41: HIDDEN WORDS
You can find the following materials hidden among the sentences:
1. Cotton
2. Suede
3. Denim
4. Leather
5. Linen

42: ADD-A-LETTER
Add the letter D to make the following words:

DEAR	LAIRD
MINDER	GRIND
WIDTH	DREAD
DRINK	DONE

43: CODEBREAKER

44: STEP BY STEP
FARE
1. FARM
2. FORM
3. FOAM
ROAM

45: OPPOSITES ATTRACT

LOSE	DISCOVER
BENEATH	ABOVE
CONCEALED	OVERT
SELFISH	GENEROUS

46: INSIDE OUT

ESTEEMED	ANTEATER
EMPLOYER	DELIVERY
ASBESTOS	UNSTABLE

47: MISSING LETTERS

48: IN A STEW
1. STILTON
2. PARMESAN
3. CHEDDAR
4. CAMEMBERT

CHAPTER 5

1: ADD-A-LETTER

Add the letter M to make the following words.

PALM	TIME
LIMP	CLAMP
MORE	PUMP
MEAT	CAMP

2: HIDDEN WORDS

You can find the following fish hidden among the sentences.
1. Trout
2. Salmon
3. Perch
4. Tench
5. Herring

3: ODD ONE OUT

CARPET.
Because it is the only one that can't be opened.

4: FIRST AND LAST

FORM	MOUNT
EGO	OINK
GOON	NIGHT
CHILD	DREAM
MEDIA	AROUND
CLAY	YELL

New word = MONDAY

5: PAIR WORDS

SOL. 1	SOL. 2	
TANK	VEHICLE	TRACTOR
CASTLE	TURRET	TANK
BANK	SAND	CASTLE
RIVER	RIPARIAN	BANK
BRIDGE	SEVERN	RIVER
CARDS	YARBOROUGH	BRIDGE
WOOD	JACK	CARDS
BOW	YEW	WOOD
BULLS-EYE	ARROW	BOW
TRACTOR	FARM	BULLS-EYE

6: WHEEL SPIN

The letter V replaces the question mark to make the word AVENUE.

7: NEXT-IN-LINE

The word JUDGE follows on as the second letter in each word is A, E, I, O and U.

8: LINK WORDS

The link word is SERVICE.
SERVICE STATION   SERVICE CHARGE
DINNER SERVICE   SECRET SERVICE
CIVIL SERVICE   SERVICE ROAD

9: X-WORDS

GRAY
PINK
GOLD

10: CODEBREAKER

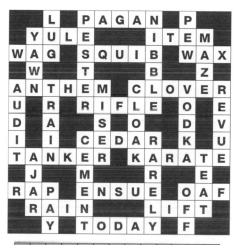

11: SCRAMBLED

1. NOTHING
2. DENTIST
3. FREEWAY
4. CARTOON
5. FLORIST
6. RECTANGLE
7. ACTRESS
8. ESCALATOR
9. PRETTY
10. STALLION
11. BARRIER
12. RESTAURANT

12: FIVE STAR

1. M (THUMB)
2. N (ANKLE)
3. H (CHEST)

13: ROGUE WORD

THANK
The other words all mean the same thing.

14: JIG-SAW JUMBLE

```
O U C H I R A T E
U N L I M I T E D
S T O M P D O N G
T I G H T O N C E
P E T O A F E A R
A P R O N F I N E
S L E P T S O F A
T E A L I E T I C
E A T A N T A R T
```

15: SCRAMBLE

GROUNDED

16: TWINS

Words left out are HOOK and TABLE.

1	2
TRIO	THREESOME
STUMBLE	TRIP
STEAL	PINCH
LETTER	EPISTLE
PLUG	BUNG
STREAM	BROOK

17: ALL CHANGE

```
P U R S E
B R A K E
S A I N T
P A S T E
C H E A T
```

CHAPTER 5

18: VOWEL PLAY

19: ANAGRAM TIMER
1. PRICE
2. PIER
3. PIE
4. RIPE
5. SPIRE

20: INCOMPLETE

21: STEP LADDER
GLAD
1. GOAD
2. GOAL
3. FOAL
FOOL

22: PROVERBS
That HAND that rocks the cradle rules the WORLD

Revenge is a dish best served COLD

MARRY in HASTE and repent in leisure

23: OPPOSITES ATTRACT
SCRUFFY	SMART
LATE	EARLY
HARD	SOFT
INTERIOR	OUTSIDE

24: MIX-UP
1. TABLE
2. CHAIR
3. SETTEE
4. SIDEBOARD

25: PICTURE THIS
PURCHASE

26: QUICK CHANGE

S	T	R	A	P
T	R	I	A	L
N	I	G	H	T
E	T	H	E	R
A	L	T	E	R

27: CROSSWORD

28: TRIANGLE TWINS
Words left out are BRAG and FETCH.

1	2
COPY	IMITATE
FALSE	BOGUS
ADORE	LOVE
MUNCH	CHEW
PERHAPS	POSSIBLY
CLAMOR	RACKET

29: STAR STRUCK
1. P (GRAPE)
2. P (APPLE)
3. P (PEACH)

30: ODDITY
CAT.
You cannot drink cats' milk!

31: DARTBOARD
BOOT, BOLD, BEAN, & BUSH.

32: FIRST & LAST
CLASH	HURRY
COLA	AROUSE
CHIMP	PACKET
SWEEP	PUZZLE
SUPPLY	YEAR

New word = HAPPY

33: LINK UP
The link word is SERVICE.
ROOM SERVICE	CIVIL SERVICE
SECRET SERVICE	SERVICE CHARGE
SERVICE AREA	DINNER SERVICE

34: ALL MIXED UP
1. BADMINTON
2. CHARACTER
3. CONTENDER
4. ELSEWHERE
5. GEOGRAPHY
6. IDENTICAL
7. LUCRATIVE
8. NAVIGATOR
9. PARAMEDIC
10. RECOGNIZE
11. SCIENTIST
12. SEPTEMBER

CHAPTER 5

35: ABACUS
FIVE, FOUR, SIX & ONE.

36: WHAT COMES NEXT?
The word Yugoslav follows on as the last letter follows the alphabetical sequence from the end backward V, W, X, Y, and Z.

37: ANAGRAMS
TEACHER

38: BITS 'N' PIECES

39: TIME FOR AN ANAGRAM
1. CHASE
2. CASE
3. SEA
4. SEAL
5. LEADS

40: WHAT, NO VOWELS!

41: HIDDEN WORDS
You can find the following vehicles hidden among the sentences:
1. Coach
2. Glider
3. Train
4. Lorry
5. Truck

42: ADD-A-LETTER
Add the letter C to make the following words:

SCENT	CRUMBLE
COVER	PLACID
SCANDAL	MANIAC
MEDICAL	CLOCK

43: CODEBREAKER

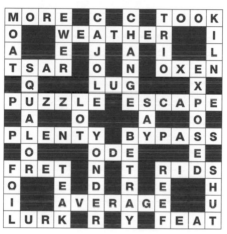

1	2	3	4	5	6	7	8	9	10	11	12	13
Q	R	X	Y	P	K	J	C	M	H	U	G	T
14	15	16	17	18	19	20	21	22	23	24	25	26
O	F	D	E	N	I	Z	V	B	S	A	L	W

44: STEP BY STEP
YEAR
1. BEAR
2. BEAT
3. BOAT
BOOT

45: OPPOSITES ATTRACT

SECRETIVE	OPEN
DUMB	WISE
SHY	EXTROVERT
NICE	ODIOUS

46: INSIDE OUT

PARAKEET	SEARCHED
CREDITOR	TOREADOR
RECENTLY	RESIDENT

47: MISSING LETTERS

48: IN A STEW
1. CAMEL
2. KANGAROO
3. DOLPHIN
4. PIGEON